PULSED MAGNETIC THERAPY

PULSED MAGNETIC THERAPY

and
Underpinning Science

Dr David C Somerville PhD CSci
FRSA

BROWN
DOG
BOOKS

Published under licence by Brown Dog Books and
The Self-Publishing Partnership, 7 Green Park Station, Bath BA1 1JB

www.selfpublishingpartnership.co.uk

ISBN printed book: 978-1-78545-144-7
ISBN e-book: 978-1-78545-145-4

Cover design by Kevin Rylands
Internal design by Andrew Easton

Printed and bound by CPI Group (UK) Ltd, Croydon CR0 4YY

Thanks to Marjorie for her constant support

Contents

Some general abbreviations used in the text

ACh	Acetylcholine
B	Tesla
$\delta\Theta$	Rate of change of magnetism
I	Current (Amperes)
L	Henries
Na	Sodium
δt	Rate of change of time reference
rbe	Relative biological effectiveness
RΩ	Resistance (Ohms)
$\delta\phi$	Rate of change of magnetic field
P	Potassium
Pmft	Pulsed Magnetic Field Therapy
V	Volts
Xl	Inductive Reactance

The copyright of this book, including all diagrams, remains with the author.

List of illustrations

Notes

Introduction

The target groups that this book is aimed at are the therapist, nurse, veterinary surgeon, physician or indeed anyone with a general or scientific interest in 'body physics'. The main aim of the book is to provide a mixture of history, therapeutic applications and science of pulsed magnetic therapy. As such the approach has been to educate, illuminate and then apply knowledge in a practical sense by discussing case histories.

Electrotherapy can be described as 'any therapy that derives its functional operation from an electrical source'. This means that where a mains supply or battery provides the power then the term electrotherapy can be applied. This does not necessarily mean that electricity is applied directly to a body to achieve a therapeutic effect. The electrical source or supply must undergo a transduction from electrical energy into various other forms such as the following:

Phototherapy - this is called several names under the generic term but generally incorrectly named as LASER for most types of applicator. The terms LILT (Low Intensity Light Therapy), cold laser, soft laser, a simple low power true LASER device, SLD (Super Luminescent Diodes that are solid state and can be made to radiate at different frequencies from low infrared to ultraviolet) come under this generic term of LASER.

Some manufacturers mix the therapy heads with LEDs and one or two small low power LASERs thereby formally justifying the term 'LASER' applicator. The efficacy of such heads in comparison to similar one comprising of LED only emitters is little researched and perhaps is more of a marketing ploy. Other devices are filament heat lamps and infrared filament devices and more latterly powerful infrared true LASERs that could be described as 'hot lasers' that are now being introduced as therapeutic devices.

Electromechanical - these can range from simple battery powered massage devices to ultrasound and shock wave applicators. These types of device are usually applied in direct physical contact with body tissue where a transfer of therapeutic electro-mechanical energy takes place in the form of high or low frequency physical vibrations.

Electro stimulation - another direct contact device is the electrical to electric stimulation type of device. These devices change the power supply, usually a low voltage battery into either a lower or voltage device called a galvanic type for micro-current stimulation across lesions, or a high pulsed voltage type used to stimulate muscles by being applied along the length of a target muscle group. The latter causes the muscle to twitch or, if applied at a higher pulsed rate, will cause muscles to contract. Application is by direct contact with specialised connector pads and electro conductive gel.

Inductive therapy – these are devices where the electrical source is changed into electromagnetic energy. These devices can be divided into those that are radiative, operating at a very high frequency to others utilising low frequency and low field devices that do not radiate. Phototherapy (see above) could arguably also belong to the radiative group since light is a form of electromagnetic energy.

Pulsed Magnetic Therapy is a form of inductive therapy that falls within the non-radiative type of transduction where a dynamic or pulsing magnetic field passes through tissue. It is whilst rising and then collapsing through tissue that therapeutic charges are induced causing changes to tissue electrics. This book is dedicated to its understanding and application. The type of injury suitable for treatment and the scientific principles involved in the use of pulsed magnetism as a main electrotherapy are discussed in depth in later chapters.

All electrotherapies need training in their use and the other electrotherapies mentioned should also not be applied without such training. It should be remembered that healing of any condition is carried out by the mechanisms and natural processes within a body. All therapies that fall under the term 'electrotherapy' may stimulate the healing process by optimising the conditions for natural processes to occur. They cannot heal in themselves.

Chapter One

PULSED MAGNETIC THERAPY

In the therapy market place there can be a bewildering choice of magnetic devices, wraps, boots and rugs. Making an informed choice requires a mixture of knowledge and understanding of their applications with regard to the conditions present or involved in therapy. It is a common trick of some salesmen to quote doubtful or non-empirical research and results to back the sale of their product. Later in this book we will look at some claims and the conditions to which magnetic therapy can be applied and those of doubtful value.

Knowledge of the electrical nature of tissue will be investigated in depth in the main part of this book but first we should look at where it can and cannot be used. All therapies given to human and animal patients should only be applied by a qualified person or under the direction of such. In veterinary use any treatment of animals other than by the owner has to be under the authority of the veterinary surgeon involved in the case (see Veterinary Surgeons Act 1962). A veterinary physiotherapist requires a condition to be diagnosed by a veterinary surgeon before treatment and only then with their approval. In human use physiotherapists are less controlled by the doctor or surgeon but the doctor in charge of the case should be made aware of any treatment to be applied.

A look at contraindications to pulsed magnetic therapy is a good way to start. One of the advantages of pulsed magnetic therapy is its benignity when used alongside other therapies and drugs. There is some anecdotal evidence of pulsed magnetic therapy enhancing the action of drugs, resulting in the reduction of the amount required (see case histories in Appendix 1). This makes it an attractive therapy for use in many conditions without generally being concerned about any side effects. Although there does not appear be any area where problems have been proven or even reported, some general safety precautions should be adhered to as much for peace of mind as for any empirical scientific basis that a condition could be made worse. The more obvious of these is tumours.

Cancer is a curse of man and animalkind and some causes of it are still not fully understood. It seems random but sometimes it seems to recur within the same family, suggesting a genetic predisposition. It is referred to in medical terms as 'neoplastic-transformation' within tissue. This simply means that cancers start with damage to the DNA in cells that may be caused by factors including chemical contamination, physical damage and different sorts of radiation. This transformation of cells usually results in the cell dying but in some cases the damaged cells begin to reproduce themselves including the damaged portion, hence forming tumours. DNA damage can occur when tissue is subjected to the overexposure of electromagnetic radiation. This is typically from X-rays or radiation from radioactive sources and UV light which have very high frequency components and it is distribution of the frequency related bursts at the subcellular level which can potentially lead to DNA damage. Pulsed Magnetic Therapy is part of an electromagnetic spectrum at the lower end, whereas X-rays and gamma rays are at the upper end. From this it is simple to deduce that energy and the ability to cause cellular damage is directly related to the part of the spectrum from which the electromagnetic radiation originates. The lower in the spectrum the less the ability to cause damage.

The question now is therefore: can sustained exposure to electromagnetic fields cause cancer? To begin to understand this, the nature of magnetic fields can be spilt into three types:

A Guide to Pulsed Magnetic Therapy

1. Static Magnetic Fields
2. Dynamic Electromagnetic Fields
3. Radiative Fields

Static magnetism will also be discussed in later chapters of this book but has no real value in therapy because it has no frequency component and therefore it is not able to transfer energy. In terms of the electromagnetic spectrum it sits at zero along with its ability to affect tissue therapeutically. The use of an extremely strong static field, as found in Magnetic Resonance Imaging (MRI) scanners, generates a magnetic field that is many thousand times stronger than any commercially available static magnet. Even in these devices no detectable effect on tissue occurs. It targets only the alignment of hydrogen molecules within the target tissue. After patients have gone through MRI investigations, no evidence of the investigation or after effects remains.

Dynamic Electromagnetic Fields: These are fields that change in intensity, rising and falling at specific rates called the frequency. The type used in Pulsed Magnetic Therapy operates generally at a frequency rate far too low to cause DNA damage. This is because the ability to transfer energy depends upon the frequency, as previously discussed. Pulsed Magnetic Therapy uses a relatively low frequency; therefore, the transferable energy is also correspondingly very low. Low frequency electromagnetism stores its energy in the fields created by coils. This energy is not lost because when the field collapses the energy is returned to the coils. As the field rises and then collapses through tissue, it causes a small charge in the tissue. This is where a little of the energy required to establish the field, or from the resistance to the collapsing field, is transferred to tissue thus forming those charges. Frequencies rise and collapse the field in the range of from 1 to 200Hz. None of the field is permanently radiated away from the producing coil or applicator.

Radiative Fields: These are very much higher frequencies than those used in Pulsed Magnetic Therapy and require an antenna to radiate energy away from them. They are sometimes called 'radiation therapy'. They can be used in certain treatments but have to have much more control and safety precautions in their application. Under controlled conditions they can be used to eliminate cancerous tissue by transferring high amounts of energy into the tumour sites to effectively kill or burn off the cancer. They also have the ability to be focussed and can be very specific in targeting tumours. The frequency used in radiative therapies falls within the radio frequency range and beyond, up to gamma frequencies at the high end of the spectrum. Uncontrolled overexposure to radio frequencies and above can in itself be carcinogenic.

It should now be obvious from the above discussion that frequencies used in pulsed electromagnetic therapy do not fall within any range that is radiative and therefore unlikely to ever be the cause of or be responsible for the spread of any existing tumour.

Pregnancy: Where pregnancy is a factor in both the therapist or patient, the same logic should apply as for tumours. It is true that foetal cells in the early stages of development are more susceptible to DNA base damage during mitosis when subjected to very high frequency electromagnetic radiation. However, established cells are around 10 times more resilient. Therapists are always cautioned that where tumours or pregnancy are involved, using pulsed magnetic therapy should be avoided. This is not necessarily because of the potential threat it may pose but more due to the psychological aspect in that if any unexplainable occurrence should happen, the client or patient will look for something to blame. However, a paper by De-Kun Lee et al (2011) suggests that exposure to dynamic magnetic fields during pregnancy may increase the possibility of asthma in offspring. The paper, taken over a 13-year period, acknowledges that the amount of exposure throughout pregnancy is difficult to assesses fully as mobile phone usage and magnetism from other sources were not necessarily measured by the instrumentation issued to the pregnant mothers. These measured field strengths at a frequency range of up 800Hz. The amount of exposure to the radio frequency band was not known. It may be that demographic trends lead to high voltage cables being located over densely populated areas, as are mobile phone masts, and these could skew the results. Also that a disproportionate number of children affected may be no greater than the population as a whole if these factors were taken into account. The paper also acknowledges that a genetic predisposition to problems in pregnancy was noted in a number of children affected.

When using pulsed magnetic therapy human nature is such that blame has to be apportioned somewhere if there is an unusual occurrence and because pulsed magnetic therapy is largely unknown to the general public it is an easy target. Exposure to large amounts of radio frequency radiation, X-rays and gamma X-rays are the main cause of tissue damage and should be avoided.

Cardiac Pacemakers. These have developed since their first introduction and modern ones today are screened against external fields that may disrupt them. However, since a very slight risk may be present and for the reasons mentioned above, it is not advisable to use pulsed magnetism where these are fitted.

SELECTING EQUIPMENT

For the physiotherapist wishing to include pulsed magnetic therapy in their treatment options, selecting equipment may be dependent upon several factors, not least of which is cost. Prices can range from a few hundred pounds to many thousands. It is not necessarily the case that the more that is spent the better and therefore more effective the equipment. Certain features need to be investigated. These are:

1. Frequencies available
2. Applicators available
3. Multi-functionality
4. Supportive scientific (preferably empirical) research and professional backup

Frequencies: The frequencies that are used in therapy have been developed from accredited research. Using the correct frequency is essential for the maximum efficacy of the application of pulsed magnetic fields. Much of the equipment available has selectable frequency ranges that give out a series of intensities and pulses of different shapes. These are square wave, saw tooth and sinusoidal. These frequencies should be able to go up to 200Hz. The choice to use waveforms other than square wave is dependant purely on the manufacturer but the most inductive is the fast rising pulse that a square wave provides. In the second part of this book this will be discussed further. The 'constant' aspect of the frequency range is called the base frequency. The other component that is desirable is the gating or pulse frequency that interrupts the base chain (see later chapters). Variable intensities are not really necessary as the induced charge is dependent upon the rise and fall rate of the field, not the maximum strength that the field establishes.

Applicators: It goes without saying that the equipment should be able to 'drive' a number of applicator types for a variety of conditions to be treated. Many applicators are in the form of 'wraps'. That is, they have two components. Each half of the wrap contains a field generator coil that is wound complementary with the other. This simply means that if the two coils are placed close together they effectively form one coil. This form of applicator is essential to apply across injured limbs, especially for a variety of orthopaedic problems. Another type of applicator is the deep penetrative type, usually in the form of a flat pad and is designed to cause the pulsating fields to extend further out into tissue. This sort of applicator is used for deep muscle or visceral injuries and is ideal for used in sacroiliac problems in horses.

The size of such applicators is also a factor in making a choice. In veterinary physiotherapy it may be that both small and large animals are likely candidates for treatment. Some applicators such as flat pads designed for sacroiliac treatment would equally be useful placed under a dog or cat bed especially if under a cushion or blanket.

Multi-functionality: Equipment electronics that power pulsed magnetic therapy applicators can also be made capable of powering phototherapy applicators and perhaps Electro Low Voltage Stimulators, provided that the settings are available for such applicators. These types of unit help reduce the equipment financial outlay and enable therapists to offer additional treatments provided they are correctly trained. Also a good feature to look at is the ability to connect more than one applicator, especially if bilateral treatments are required or using several applicators over a large area.

Supportive Scientific Backup: There are devices available that make some outlandish claims. It is essential that any claims for efficacy be backed up by clinical research. In my career I have been asked to carry out research for companies. One in particular had results that could not support the manufacturer's claims. On presenting the results I was asked if it was possible to skew these results favourably. I firmly refused, but financial incentives could influence results with others. It has to be mentioned that, although the device was electromagnetic, it wasn't pulsed magnetism in the sense of this book's subject. It should be said in the company's defence that they had a huge amount of positive anecdotal evidence but the way the research was asked to be carried out did not support it. Perhaps a different approach than the one requested may have.

Check also that the company provides a professional backup and is able to scientifically explain the processes involved in pulsed magnetic therapy.

TREATMENT CONDITIONS AND SETTINGS

Pulsed magnetic therapy lends itself to the treatment of a variety of conditions and injuries. On the Canine and Equine Physiotherapy (CEPT) course we teach pulsed magnetic therapy as a major electrotherapy with field-based practical application. For those who are not familiar with this therapy, then the rest of this chapter will hopefully give an insight into how it is used and, along with the case history appendix, allow an informed decision on whether to include it.

TREATMENT REGIMES

Treatment areas can be categorised as hard or soft tissue. These could be further sub-divided into bone, ligament and tendon, muscle and neurological injuries. Ligament and tendon injuries can be treated as for bone injures.

HARD TISSUE

Bone: In the second part of this book we look at the science behind the function and treatment of bone injuries but for the purposes of this chapter we will look at conditions and appropriate settings.

Fractures: Fractures, especially those in long bones, will heal at rates dependent upon other conditions. In the ideal situation with a healthy young patient, the rate of healing will be optimised naturally, especially if some load bearing is possible. Where this is not possible then enhancement to the healing process can be aided by pulsed magnetic therapy. The applicator selected should be the one ideal for the injury site.

If the injury is a long bone fracture, then using a wrap type applicator directly across the fracture site is the ideal. If the injury has been reduced and either a binding or plaster cast support used, then applying over and around the support will provide treatment directly through it. Pulsed magnetic fields will pass through such casts and bindings unimpeded. A constant chain of pulses at 50Hz is the ideal setting applied for 20 minutes at least twice daily. If metal implants are present, then this should not be of concern. Metal implants are made of titanium or stainless steel and as such are not ferro-magnetic. The implant will have no appreciable effect on the pulsing magnetic field nor the field be in any way detrimental.

NON-UNION FRACTURES

These fractures are normally the most difficult to resolve in that there are several factors involved, one of which is possibly neurological. Using a 50Hz constant setting as for a normal fracture may help to stimulate union. Coupling this with a constant 200Hz treatment proximal to the fracture site may help optimise the repair to any neurological damage within the bone.

Application is standard for all bone injuries and requires a minimum of a 20-minute application twice daily on a constant 50Hz setting,

Shin splints in horses are injuries associated with the remnants of the 2nd and 4th metatarsals over the cannon bone. Injuries to them originate mainly from trauma such as kicks or bumps. Swelling is a common feature. Treating with pulsed magnetic therapy on 50 base, 17.5 pulse may help reduce this swelling. If actual injury has occurred to the bone, then the 50Hz therapy should be followed as above.

OTHER BONE INJURIES

Fig 1.

Typical application

Trauma to smaller bones such as ribs are all treated the same as the long bones. Incidences of non-union in these bones are rarely reported so veterinary physiotherapists or surgeons should monitor treatment by gentle palpation, looking for any swelling in the area. If the patient shows evidence of chronic pain, then pulsed magnetic therapy on a setting of 200Hz may reduce it allowing palpation if the area is particularly sensitive. Discussion on pain treatment follows in the neurological discussion section.

SOFT TISSUE

We have already alluded to the possibility of reduction of swelling around shin splints. Injuries that result in swelling can be treated differently in the two phases of acute and chronic. In the acute phase, if caught just after the initial trauma such as a blow or kick, then application at 50Hz base on 5Hz pulse may cause vaso-constriction, that is tightening and closing of the capillaries in the affected area and may reduce overall swelling. Since pain can result not just from the initial injury but also due to pressure caused by the swelling, then rapid treatment may reduce both the swelling and subsequent pain. If the swelling is at the chronic stage, then a setting of 50Hz on a pulse of 17.5 may cause vaso-dilation to reduce pressure and also help remove fluid.

Muscular injuries may have three aspects: tissue damage, neurological damage and swelling. The swelling should be treated separately as before, choosing the setting as to whether judged as acute or chronic. Normal processes of healing may also be enhanced using the same setting as for a chronic swollen phase. It may help where cellular damage has occurred. Neurological damage may exhibit two aspects, pain and numbness. Both are treated using 200Hz on a constant setting. Some numbness may be due to severance of small sensory nerves in and around the injury or lesion. These will eventually reconnect restoring normal sensation but may be optimised in this process by the 200Hz application.

Pulsed Magnetic Therapy has no effect on acute pain since the fast neural pathways are different to those sending chronic signals. Pulsed Magnetic Therapy applied over the area of damaged tissue which is causing the chronic pain will reduce the perception of it by effectively blocking the activation of slow neural pathways. The application in all situations of soft tissue injuries should be for a minimum of 10 minutes, repeated with a minimum of 4 hours between treatments. This allows the changes in tissue due to the application of the therapy to cycle back to pre-treatment levels. The above recommendations for both soft and hard tissue treatments have a scientific basis and in the following chapters are discussed in depth.

The regimes are not exhaustive and it may be that therapists develop their own sequences for conditions presented. The following table is given as a general guide to treatments:

A Guide to Pulsed Magnetic Therapy

Damaged Tissue	Base Frequency	Pulsed Frequency	Timing of Treatment (minimum)
Bone	50	Constant	20 mins
Ligaments	50	17.5 Hz	10 mins
Muscle	50	17.5 Hz	10 mins
Swelling (Acute)	50	5 Hz	10 mins
Swelling (Chronic)	50	17.5	10 mins
Lesions	50	17.5	10 mins
Neurological Damage	200	Constant	10 mins
Pain (Chronic)	200	Constant	10 mins

Settings Table 1

Although I have tended to lean the discussions towards the veterinary application, the same would apply to human treatments although shin splints in humans are mainly a problem in the tibia due to over-exercise. This is sometimes termed 'medial tibial syndrome'. Combinations of the above may be used e.g. using a vasodilation setting prior to treatment for orthopaedic treatments may increase the blood flow to the area. The same would apply to neurological treatments.

TREATMENT OF INFECTIONS

Where a bacterial infection exists pulsed magnetic therapy is not generally recommended. This is due to the possibility of increased blood flow to and from the area. This may spread the infection although anecdotally some experienced therapists suggest that one initial treatment may be therapeutic.

APPLICATION AROUND THE HEAD AND CHEST

Some research has been carried out on the effects of pulsed magnetic therapy for brain neurological conditions such as Dementia and Parkinson's disease. There have been mixed results where the intensity of the pulsing field has been extremely low. Sandyk (1993) researched the therapeutic effects using pico-tesla, extremely low intensity pulses. These are much lower than used in general therapy treatments, however many reports suggest beneficial effects. Some involve horses with 'head-shaking syndrome'. Applying a small applicator over the horse's forehead and on a setting of 17.5Hz pulse on a 50Hz base frequency is thought to vaso-dilate capillaries within the frontal lobes of the horse's brain. This may help to help clear away toxins that may be one of the causes of this behavioural problem. Reported results have been very positive and this area is prime for further research.

Such reports of this ability to open up capillaries would seem to also apply to the alveoli within the lungs. After receiving reports where it had been used to treat back pain, patients who were also asthmatic sufferers reported to their physiotherapist that they experienced some relief for a period of time after the back pain application. Although these reports came from an Australian colleague, we followed this through with a simple trial using asthmatic students at a UK sports college. This involved treating a small group of asthmatic student volunteers on a weekly basis. This was with the involvement and overall supervision of a thoracic consultant from the local main hospital. It involved having subjects report their wellbeing following pulsed magnetic therapy applied to their backs. We carried out a simple analysis of a questionnaire about the use of the inhalers for a period of time straight after the treatment. This did seem to confirm the hypothesis. It has to be said that the numbers were too small to give any scientific credence but it does seem to fit in with the theory and this will be discussed in detail later in this book. Due to circumstances beyond our control we were unable to set up a larger and more controlled trial. The settings used were again 17.5 pulse gating a 50Hz base frequency square wave of an electromagnetic field applied by a flat applicator. This was similar to the one discussed earlier.

GENERAL DISCUSSION

Although this first chapter has so far attempted to give an insight into the practical application of pulsed magnetic therapy and has presented a very positive picture of its use, it should never be regarded as a treatment regime alone. It can be used alongside other forms of treatment where medicaments have been prescribed and should never replace them without the medical or veterinary professionals' say so. When treating any condition with pulsed magnetic therapy it is important to apply on a regular basis of at least twice daily. Our asthmatic research could have been improved by increasing the number of weekly applications more than once per week event that was run. The effectiveness is believed to be enhanced by this regular application, with research suggesting that the effects last about four hours. This sets the gap time between treatments as it allows the treated area to 'cycle' from being stimulated back to the pre-treatment level. Oxygen (partial) levels in tissue were also found to be much higher after treatment by as much as 200%. This remained elevated for up to eight hours before returning to normal again. This follows a 10-minute application

TIMING

The treatment times suggested in the table are a minimum set to achieve a saturation effect. Movement of the applicator and readjustment may add several minutes to a specific area to achieve the maximum. Overdosing by going well beyond the recommended treatment time is not detrimental to the condition being treated but will have no greater effect, as once saturation levels have been achieved they cannot be added to. The 10-minute suggested time is recommended minimum for all soft tissue injuries. Orthopaedic injuries do not have an upper limit to application since the treatment mimics natural effects that stimulate healing, without load bearing, especially in the acute phase. Timing for orthopaedics is therefore based on comfort and the 20-minute treatment suggestion reflects this.

There is no evidence that overexposure to tissue or any condition by low frequency pulsed magnetism has any detrimental effect. Workers in steel smelting mills are constantly exposed to extremely strong alternating fields without any negative effect. An elderly gentleman who was personally known to us, worked in such mills in Sheffield and claimed they had a beneficial side to them. He died peacefully at the age of 93 having had very few illnesses in his life. He made the statement to me just before he died and in the knowledge of my ongoing interest in the subject, that "magnetic fields were god's gift to mankind". Whether by a god or nature, magnetic fields are a natural phenomenon and when used dynamically, are useful aids to helping many conditions to heal.

It has been suggested that the dynamic interaction with the earth's magnetic field is an essential part of our environment. The natural field produced by the earth is far from static and movement within this slightly dynamic field may have caused an evolutionary dependence on it. Gregoriev suggested that after screening rabbits in a magnetic field-free chamber they became osteoporotic. They quickly returned to normal once exposed to their normal environment.

Chapter Two

HISTORICAL REVIEW

There is virtually no area of modern life that is not directly affected by dynamic magnetism, including trains, trams, cars, aeroplanes, TVs, electricity supplies from all sources and all of the devices and products they power. We would have to go back to pre-industrialised society to find any time that did not make use of this seemingly mysterious force. Even then there was some use of its properties as will be discussed below. In medicine its use as a diagnostic tool is well established with Magnetic Resonance Imaging. Using magnets directly as a specific tool for its curative properties has to be viewed with scepticism. There are no magic bullets and despite many claims about them being attached to the body or worn as bracelets, no empirical research has ever verified their efficacy.

The first chapter of this book looked at pulsed magnetic therapy from a user perspective. The second onwards starts to underpin the science behind it and to justify its use as a mainstream therapy.

This book investigates how it is possible to use magnetic fields that pulsate and cause the induction of small electric charges within the body in much the same way that a rotating and, therefore, oscillating magnetic field induces an electric charge in a generator to provide domestic power. The term 'dynamic magnetism' is therefore appropriate wherever therapeutic magnetism is referred to in this book.

Electrotherapies, as previously discussed and of which pulsed magnetic therapy is becoming a major player, have their origins in the history of electricity. Not specifically as therapies but from an effect noted and recorded by the ancient Greek philosopher Thales around 600 BC. Thales was a pre-

Socratic Greek philosopher from Miletus in Asia Minor. The Greek word for amber is 'Elektron' (ἤλεκτρον) and it was an effect noted by him that if amber is rubbed with a material such as wool, fine linens or silks then these become attracted and pulled towards and cling to it for a while. As a philosopher, it would have been very difficult for him to explain the phenomenon without the theoretical reasoning we have today about matter, and so it became known as the triboelectric' effect from the Greek 'tribo' meaning to rub and 'electric' from the word for amber. Another philosopher one hundred and forty years later, called Democritus, theorised that if a solid object was cut in half and one of the halves was further cut in half and the process repeated and repeated over and over again, there would come a point when the minute particle that remained could be reduced no longer. This he called 'Atomus', meaning indivisible. Although philosophers such as Aristotle are said to have dismissed these theories as worthless, these great thinkers could probably have not known that the triboelectric effect and the atomus would be inextricably linked and, in the future, become the basis of the theory of matter in physics, chemistry and magnetism.

Atoms, and knowledge of their structures, consisting of protons, neutrons and electrons form the basis of our understanding of all elements and molecules. The common binding factor for all structures is the smallest of the three general components making up atoms, the electron. The story of the electron and a basic understanding of its nature is essential to understanding matter. Since the electron is a fundamental and integral part of the atom, its ability to exchange places with the electrons of neighbouring atoms when certain conditions prevail forms the basis of electricity and how electrical and electronic components function.

The effect noted by Thales is the electrostatic attraction caused by electrons being removed from the surface of the amber by the friction of rubbing with fur. This leads to the situation in which the amber becomes unnaturally deficient in electrons. Losing electrons in this way is said to make the amber positively charged. Having less electrons, it then physically attracts the fur or silks to it in order to balance out to a neutral state, by recovering the lost electrons. The same effect can be observed when, in dry weather, a nylon silk or cotton garment is removed and a series of spits are heard and the garments become clingy. In the dark it is possible to observe small flashes of light. These occur as the charges created by friction cause the displaced electrons to try to balance out by jumping across small gaps. This further causes a flash of light by ionising the air, in the same way, but on a very small scale, that lightning also does. Pulsed Magnetic Therapy owes its existence and affects to the electron and the properties it possesses and in the following discussions this, one of the most important and fundamental of particles, is highlighted. If the reader is not familiar with the terms used above such as *ionising*, and the concept of *negative* and *positive* charges, then these will be covered in the following chapters.

In any therapy applied to both humans or animals it is important to understand the electrical nature of matter in order to further understand the interactions of electrotherapies and how they may be beneficial to assist injured or diseased biological mechanisms to repair. The need for a deeper understanding of physics or chemistry is not required at this stage and will be built up as the reader, without a scientific background, progresses through the sections. A spiral technique has been used in this book. This means that facts and statements used in the early chapters are revisited as the reader progresses through the book. This reoccurring theme helps to build up the learning and the understanding of context of differing parts of the subject. I would recommend that the reader becomes familiar with Faraday's laws of magnetism and induction as this will aid further understanding in the following chapters.

As the author I promised, when asked by many people to write this book, to keep it as straightforward as possible whilst maintaining the scientific information essential for those interested in further studies.

Chapter Three

THE SCIENCE: BACK TO BASICS

To understand pulsed electromagnetism both in how it is produced and how it interacts with biological systems, there is a need to refresh or become more familiar with the basic nature of matter. Most people are familiar with the concept of the atom from basic science teaching in secondary schools. For those readers who did not progress further with physics or chemistry then some background reading is recommended. For the purposes of this book a level no greater than upper secondary school physics is required.

Atoms are the smallest of particles in which an element can exist so the Greek theory of the 'atomus' is partially correct. However, all elements are made of atoms that have the same building blocks but differing combinations of electrons, protons and neutrons that form them. Electrons (Leptons in quantum physics) orbit the protons and neutrons that form the nucleus of each atom. It is common to think of the orbit as something similar on the macro scale to the earth moon combination. The moon, a solid ball, is attracted to a very much larger earth by the force of gravity but its rotational energy or centrifugal force keeps it orbiting all of the time instead of falling towards the earth. This combination has equivalence to the simplest atom, hydrogen. This consists of one proton and one electron. See Fig 2. The macro-micro comparison stops there as the electron is a minute entity in no way comparable in size to the nucleus as the moon is to the earth. It is a particle almost of pure energy that has also virtually zero mass. It is so energetic it cannot be held still in that although attracted to the nucleus, it orbits around it in a manner that causes its precession around the nucleus.

A Guide to Pulsed Magnetic Therapy

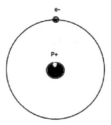

Fig 2. Styalised hydrogen atom

The precession and orbit of the electron forms a 'cloud' by being virtually everywhere in orbit around the nucleus at the same time, due to its rotational and spin speed. A simple two-dimensional analogy illustrates this by the fact that an aircraft propeller when spinning at high revolutions per minute is virtually in all parts of the disc it forms due to its rotation, although the blades of the propeller occupy only a small space within that disc.

The proton is the other, but very much larger, particle forming part of the nucleus. It tries to pull electrons to it through 'electrostatic' attraction. We term the proton as being electrostatically positive (+) and the electron negative (-). Since on the macro scale the moon has rotational energy and overcomes the earth's gravitational pull by orbiting, the electron similarly overcomes the electrostatic attraction of the nucleus by rotating around it at high speed, forming the electron cloud. In the hydrogen atom the nucleus consists of one proton. The proton is less energetic but of much higher mass, but having an equal and opposite charge to one electron, so that the overall charge of one electron orbiting one proton is zero. The charges cancel out as far as any other electron or charged particle is concerned. Of course elements have differing numbers of electrons and protons, but as long as there are equal numbers of each then a neutrally charged atom will exist.

The other fundamental particle is the neutron, as mentioned above, which, along with proton, is referred to as a 'nucleon'. As its name suggests, the neutron does not have an electrostatic charge. It is in fact a proton with a 'captured electron'. The combination of the two particles cancelling out any charge gives the neutron a slightly larger mass than the proton. The proton and the neutron are held together in every nucleus by a strong nuclear force.

These particles also form part of the nucleus in larger atoms and generally equal the number of protons and electrons. In terms of mass, these atoms have an atomic weight and are usually defined by the number of nucleons within each nucleus. From this is derived the 'atomic mass unit' (amu), see below, and equates to $1/12^{th}$ the weight of a solitary (unbounded) carbon-12 atom. It is not the intention in this book to delve deep into nuclear physics but suffice to say that a carbon 12 atom has a nucleus of 6 protons and 6 neutrons. $1/12^{th}$ of this totalling a weight of:

$$1.66053892 \times 10^{-27} \text{ kilograms.}$$

The addition of an extra electron in a proton gives the extremely slight difference in weight between neutrons and protons. By taking the weight of 6 protons and 6 neutrons, as in a carbon atom, and dividing by 12 we arrive at the above value for the atomic mass unit.

The atomic number of any individual atom, as distinct from the atomic mass unit, is simply the total of the number of protons and neutrons in the nucleus. The 6 electrons orbiting the nucleus of the carbon atom are generally regarded in relative terms as insignificant although the mass of one electron is given as:

$$0.000548 \text{ amu or } 9.1093826(16) \times 10^{-31} \text{ kilogram.}$$

Electrons exist at different levels of the cloud and in their perpetual energetic and quantum state repel other electrons. The electron cloud or level closest to the nucleus occupies a smaller area and so only a maximum of two electrons could exist at this level and so form a 'shell'. Other electrons attracted to the nucleus have to exist at a higher level at a distance repelled sufficiently by the first level negative electron cloud (shell) but still with an overriding attraction to the nucleus.

A Guide to Pulsed Magnetic Therapy

It is important to understand that the terms *energy level*, *shell* and *cloud* are really different ways of describing where electrons orbit in specific numbers relative to the distance from, and around the nucleus of, their parent atom.

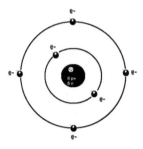

Fig 3. Representative diagram of a carbon atom

The cloud forming a 'shell' at the next level of electrons can allow more than just two electrons in the next shell. In fact, a total of 8 electrons could form this cloud. In the carbon-12 atom this second level is called the valence (outer level) and has just 4 electrons although that level could theoretically hold 8, as above. Carbon (see Fig 3) is a very stable element in itself although some carbon atoms are known as isotopes and are unstable because they have 2 extra neutrons within the nucleus. These are Carbon 14 atoms and it is to the random decay of these atoms ejecting the extra neutrons that the science of carbon dating owes its origins. This random decay is a way of describing how a carbon isotope eventually returns to being a normal carbon atom by ejecting those extra nucleons.

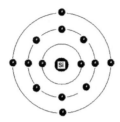

Fig 4. Silicon atom

Heavier elements such as silicon, Fig 4 above, have an atomic number of 28, meaning 14 neutrons and 14 protons. It also has 14 electrons orbiting. The distribution of electrons follows the order as described with the two electrons at the inner level, eight at the second level and four at the outer (valence) level. As the electrons orbit in their clouds at levels further from the nucleus they are said to have a higher energy state and are less strongly attracted to the nucleus.

The outer energy state of an element such as silicon is also termed the valence state in which a total of 18 electrons could also theoretically also fit or share with adjacent atoms. The various energy levels are referred to as 'shell numbers' and given designator letters: n=1 (K) is level 1 closest to the nucleus and known as the 'ground state', n=2 (L) with the maximum total of 8 electrons, n=3 (M) this is the outer valent level for silicon, n=4 (N), n=5 (O) and n=6 (P). The heavier elements fill up each level with specific maximum numbers of electrons. This follows a pattern n= 1 (2), n=2 (8), n=3 (18), n=4 (32), n=5 (50), n=6 (72). There is a wonderful symmetry with cloud distribution of electrons that can be simply calculate from the formula:

$$2n^2$$

Where n is the energy level i.e.

Level (ground state) $= 1^2$ x 2 $=2$

level $2 = 2^2$ x 2 = 8

level 3 = 3^2 x 2 = 18

level 4 = 4^2 x 2 = 32

and so on.....

In the form of a table this would be:

Energy level	Shell ID	Electrons per Shell (maximum)
1	K	2
2	L	8
3	M	18
4	N	32
5	O	50
6	P	72

Table 2. Table of energy levels and the maximum capacity of electrons that can exist within that level

Hydrogen, the simplest atom, is always found in a dual state of H_2 because, although in its basic elemental state it only has one electron, by sharing with another hydrogen atom the ground state shell becomes effectively full. Each atom shares the other's electron thereby fulfilling a maximum within that state making a stable bond and a hydrogen molecule. With elements such as carbon and silicon the outer energy levels are not filled to their maximum capacity having just 4 electrons. This means that they can share the electrons with adjacent atoms, fulfilling their need to remain neutrally charged but having an effect of a fuller and more stable outer shell. Electrons from other carbon or silicon atoms continually exchange places. This makes it seem that at any one time there are eight electrons in the outer shell. This is called 'co-valent bonding'.

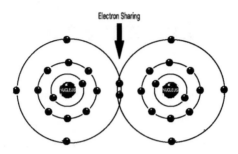

Fig 5. Simple co-valent bonding

The illustration in Fig 5 shows just two silicon atoms overlapping their outer valence shells allowing electrons to exchange orbits. In a crystal lattice of silicon, the same sharing will occur in three dimensions with each valence electron in each atom exchanging electrons with adjacent ones in all directions. Co-valent bonding of atoms is very stable and under normal circumstances causes them to bond together to form lattices. Many other materials and elements bond this way and an appreciation of this is a necessary part of understanding the electrical properties of biological materials such as bone.

It should now be obvious that the electron, even though very small, plays an important part in the holding together and bonding of elements and matter throughout the universe and could be called a 'god' particle, although that title has been recently attached to the 'Higgs-Boson' particle in quantum physics. The discussion of that branch of science is way beyond the scope needed in this book. Although study of the electron itself is part of deeper science, it is the effects of transitory electrons and their nature that the therapist may become more familiar with to begin to understanding pulsed magnetic interactions.

Chapter Four

WHAT IS MAGNETISM?

There are many misconceptions about the nature of magnetism. I have heard many times people expressing a view that "nobody knows what magnetism is or how it works in therapy". One manufacturer even advertises "nobody knows how a miracle works but our devices are miraculous". Statements like this are somewhat misleading, showing ignorance and reflecting long held beliefs that magnetism is somehow a mysterious force verging on the supernatural. Hopefully this chapter will start to unravel the mystery in which magnets and magnetism are held.

Magnetism has become synonymous with attraction in many senses. 'They have a magnetic personality' is commonly in use to indicate a pleasant demeanour of someone easy to get along with and who also attracts many friends. Magnets also are repulsive but it is the attraction characteristic that seems to be the one that most associate with them. Repulsion can be demonstrated when two magnets are brought together with the same poles facing each other. They will physically repel each other whilst opposite poles will attract. Both magnetic attraction and repulsion have equal prominence in how they are used in a way that makes a magnetic field useful in both industrial uses and in therapy. Static magnets are useful in small electric motors to provide a field that a rotor producing its own dynamic electromagnetic field can be attracted to and react against. In generators a static field can provide an environment for a rotating coil to interact with, causing a current to be 'induced' into it. Static magnets by themselves cannot provide useful motion or the generation of electricity and always have to have a moving (dynamic) component interacting with them.

A Guide to Pulsed Magnetic Therapy

Used in therapy, magnetic fields themselves must also be dynamic to be of any use, as will be discussed later.

The term 'magnetism' is thought to have originated 4000 years ago and been discovered by a shepherd called Magnes. It is now part of legend that, when herding his sheep, he found that iron nails in his boots and the iron parts of his staff, became firmly attracted to and attached to the rock he was standing on. The rock was said to be dark in colour. The legend further suggests that he dug up the earth around the rock and found other similar stones that were then named 'Lodestones' meaning 'lead' or 'attract' stones. As with many of the ancient Greek discoveries, this magnetic material was given the name of Magnetite either after the area of Magnesia or after the man who discovered it. We now know that magnetite is a naturally occurring magnetic material made up of crystals formed of compounds of iron and oxygen atoms. Three iron atoms bonded with four oxygen atoms give the chemical formula, Fe_3O_4 where Fe_3 is 3 iron atoms and O_4, the 4 oxygen atoms. How magnets attract iron and attract or repel other magnets will be discussed later but for now the intention is to try and understand exactly what magnetism is and it is to the electron that we have to look to gain this understanding. The ability of electrons to share orbits within molecular structures is a key to the understanding of how these transitory electrons cause magnetic fields to form. Electrons will happily orbit their atoms at various energy levels and follow the rules discussed in Chapter Three. The higher energy levels have more electrons and are held less tightly to their parent nucleus by electrostatic attraction. It was also discussed that electrons can share orbits with adjacent atoms by co-valent bonding of atoms of the same element and similarly configured adjacent atoms. In the case of oxygen, one oxygen atom will bond with another because of having 6 electrons in the outer shell. The two atoms bond by sharing two electrons making the shell of each atom effectively full with the complement of 8 which is the stable state.

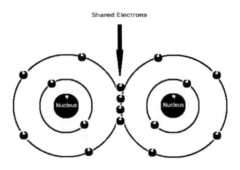

Fig 6. Oxygen molecule

Thus the two oxygen atoms become an oxygen O_2 molecule. They can also share electrons with other elements such as iron. Iron has 26 electrons (amu of iron is 56 having 30 neutrons within its nucleus and 26 protons) with only two electrons in its outer shell or cloud. Oxygen has only two energy levels, ground state with 2 electrons and 6 electrons in the second. By bonding with the iron atom it shares the two outer electrons of iron so that the oxygen fills the maximum it can have in its outer second level shell. This is called Ferric oxide FO(I) and this is a further example of co-valent bonding and it is this bonding that is used in blood to combine 'haems' (ionic iron molecules) with oxygen within the lung. In magnetite three iron atoms bond with 4 oxygen atoms in this way, around a very much larger structure forming the molecule of sharing electrons.

The other form of bonding (Ionic Bonding) occurs when one atom loses one of its outer electrons unbalancing the charge so becoming a positive (+) ion, and another gains an electron so becoming a negative (-) ion. The two are then attracted by the opposite charges.

This ionisation may be caused through heat or another oppositely charged ion that attracts an electron away from its parent atom. In other cases, it may be that highly positive electrostatic charges, such as batteries and power supplies, cause electrons to leave their nucleus, or collisions with other atoms cause the losses. In the cases where sodium loses an electron, becoming a positive ion (Na^+), it is then known as a 'cation' (pronounced cat-ion) with the + sign indicating the absence of one electron. Ions are created not just by the loss of an electron but also by unnaturally gaining an electron in similar ways. The transfer of the electron from sodium to chlorine causes chlorine to become a negative ion (Cl^-) known as an 'anion' and negatively charged. The net result is that these two oppositely charged ions will come together by the attraction of opposite charges thereby neutralising the overall charge, and thus becoming a Na^+Cl^- molecule, common salt.

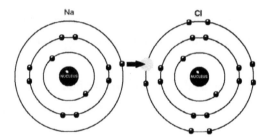

Fig 7. Ionic bonding forming common salt - sodium chloride

It is not the intention of this book to become over involved in the chemistry of structures but to give a flavour of the transitory nature of electrons within such structures and in a 3-dimensional manner. The molecule shown above will also share electrons with other molecules and in all directions forming a very much larger structure called a crystal.

The same applies to iron where outer electrons are less tightly bonded and the crystals form structures that are called 'domains'. These contain many trillions of iron molecules all actively sharing electrons that form minute currents around the domain. It is these natural currents that form the basis of phenomena called a 'static magnetic field' and will be covered further in this chapter.

Magnetic fields have been used by humans for millennia. Vikings and ancient Chinese are said to have used lodestones to navigate the seas by suspending small pieces of them, noting that when loosely suspended it would always adopt a north-south alignment along the earth's magnetic field, roughly pointing at the Pole Star.

There are many unsubstantiated claims that the magnetic properties of lodestone have therapeutic effects and were used as far back as Cleopatra's time in ancient medicine. Many minerals and crystals were also claimed to have wonderful properties of healing and many people to this day still believe it. The beauty of crystals including magnetite is without question and perhaps owning such objects would make anyone feel good. This placebo effect is probably the most likely cause of healing as no empirical scientific proof exists to the contrary.

To be able to understand how a magnetic field from any source can be of medical use we first have to understand what causes the field and how to interact with it. In heavy materials such as iron there exists bonded numbers of atoms forming an electron sharing micro-crystal. Groups of these crystals have a magnetic alignment and are called 'Domains'. Electrons, being highly energetic and negatively charged, can only exist around atoms in energy levels as discussed in Chapter Three. Outer electrons at the higher energy state easily lose electrons that form part of a movement or 'flow' from atom to atom.

An atom momentarily losing an electron will become a positively charged ion until another electron from along the flow will fill the vacancy neutralising the atom again. The electron, still being highly energetic, will normally only allow other electrons within a certain distance because of the same charge being present. Electrons will therefore repel other electrons. The crystal structure aligns and causes the flow of electrons to be in one direction. Electrons, due to the complexity of the crystal, are somewhat unnaturally being forced in this one direction allowing other electrons to close in. This proximity along the line of flow causes a reaction that is manifested at right angles to the flow: this is a magnetic field. In un-magnetised iron the domains are aligned randomly so that the small field generated by one domain is opposed and therefore cancelled out by another. The net effect is that in all directions there is no discernible net magnetic field.

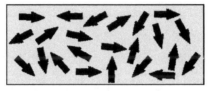

Fig 8. Random domain alignment (No field)

If the iron is then subjected to a strong magnetic field along its length the domains will begin to align and all their fields will have the same north-south alignment and add together.

The result of this is that a magnetic field will become permanently established for as long as the domains align. See Fig 9 and Fig 10 below. Heat or physical shocks will cause the domains to randomise again and the overall magnetic field will be lost.

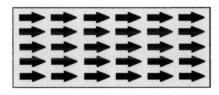

Fig 9. Magnetic domains aligned

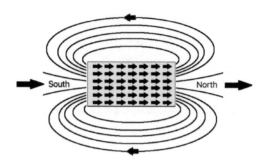

Fig 10. Domains aligned (Field formed)

In other metals similar domains exist, but more tightly held ones, and a magnetic field can be established in the same way but then reverts back to the random alignment when the external magnetic influence is removed. Electromagnetic relays use this property.

Having established how magnetic fields may occur due to a drift of electrons in one direction it is now useful to understand how, in the case of magnetism caused by a current-carrying wire, energy is stored in the magnetic field it produces. This can be simply reasoned by using the water analogy. Water is generally an uncompressible fluid. When applied under pressure along a pipe, there will be a force exerted in the direction of flow and also at right angles. If the pipe is made of an expandable material, then the diameter of the pipe will increase in proportion to the pressure applied: see diagram below.

A Guide to Pulsed Magnetic Therapy

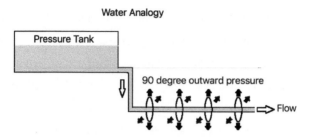

Fig 11 Water analogy

The water analogy, illustrated in Fig 11 above, shows that some of the energy involved in the pressure of flow may be stored in the walls of an expandable pipe. When the pressure is removed the energy stored is returned to the water remaining in the pipe. In the body this sideways pressure is made use of in the aorta. As the high systolic pressure pulse is delivered from the heart, the aorta expands at 90° to the blood flow. This stores some of the energy from the pulse that is then returned to the blood flow as it enters the diastolic phase. It does in fact smooth the flow somewhat, resulting in a gentler pulse but maintaining the pressure longer.

The above analogies have a relevance to electrons in that when a pressure is applied as an electric charge (represented by the pressure tank), negative at one end and positive at the other end of a wire, electrons will 'flow' along the wire. This 'pressure' causes a reaction because of the repulsion of electrons with each other represented by uncompressible water, so causing a magnetic field to store energy at 90° to the direction of flow. When the electric charge is removed, the energy stored is returned into the wire, momentarily affecting the electrons within the wire and this effect is called a 'back electromotive force'.

Electrons also have a spin property in that, though highly energetic, they also spin. It is this property that may be the cause of the magnetic field having a perceived polarity that, unlike the water analogy, only has a unified pressure.

With a static magnet the outward pressure, now called a field, is always there unless the magnetised material is de-magnetised. The most obvious effect of a static magnet is that of attraction in that in certain metals, where domains can be either temporarily or permanently aligned, the fields will try to combine. Where the domains are in opposite alignment then there is repulsion. This attraction or repulsion is linked directly back to the electrostatic attraction and repulsion within the crystalline structure of the domains.

In discussing magnetism so far the focus has been on natural magnetism derived from molecular structures that are unchanged under normal circumstances. We now move on to magnetic fields, alluded to above, that are both transitory and dynamic: electromagnetism.

Where changing magnetic fields exist there is always another component called the 'electric charge'. This is the prime mover of electrons in transit and exists because of the imbalance of electrons. This can be caused by chemical reactions as in batteries or by dissimilar metals. In crystalline structures the driving force behind the flow of electrons comes from bonded atoms and the electrostatic forces within the structures. The fields generated from electron flow within crystalline structures are static and unchanging, therefore are called permanent magnetic fields. If electrons are forcibly caused to flow along a wire, then an electric force is required to cause this to occur. When batteries supply such a charge and a flow of electrons occurs through a conductor, a magnetic field produced is now called an 'electromagnetic' field.

Essentially, it is important to understand that a magnetic field from any source is the same in nature, but different in its ability to change polarity or switch on and off. Electrons orbiting atoms in a wire randomly exchange places and are still highly energetic. There is no overall 'drift' along the wire. An electric charge, being negative at one end of the wire and positive at the other, causes the electrons to 'drift' to the positive by being attracted by the positive charge and the flow maintained by being resupplied by the negative end. This applied charge changes the electron activity from a random state producing no magnetic field, to a more orderly flow that will produce a field.

In a static magnet the strength of the field produced is dependent upon the number of domains that align. In a wire the field strength is directly proportional to the number of electrons drifting along the wire that is in turn influenced by the resistance of the wire, temperature and the amount of 'pressure' from electric charge available. Electromagnetism, therefore, is not fixed but variable in its intensity. It is this variable or 'dynamic' property that derives its usefulness as a modality used in therapy.

It is normal in physics to talk of electron flow rather than drift. The word drift conjures up in the mind a slow saunter along the wire but in reality this occurs at near light speed. It is the pressure caused by the electric charge that causes the effect of producing a magnetic field as previously discussed.

At this point, introducing a few facts and figures may help the reader to grasp the sheer quantity of electrons 'drifting' in an electric current:

A set quantity of electrons is defined by a specific number: 6.24×10^{18} or to be more precise: 624150965000000000 electrons. This amount is called a 'Coulomb'. One coulomb of electrons entering and leaving the same conductor per second equals a current of 1 Amp. It is useful to put this number into context by comparing the number of average size grains of sand on all the beaches of the earth. Someone took the trouble to measure the area and depth of all the beaches and then calculate the number of grains of sand. This is reckoned to be around 7.5×10^{18} grains of sand. In comparison, the number of electrons in a coulomb is just short of the equivalent of all the grains of sand on earth when just one amp is flowing. It is also an interesting fact that just one grain of sand contains more atoms and electrons than there are grains of sand on earth's beaches.

Electrons, although vast in quantity, do not have an easy path through materials. Tightly bonded atoms in crystal structures allow relatively few electrons to flow or drift through them. These are said to be highly resistive. Even in good conductive materials such as iron and copper, whose atom's outer electrons are easily made to drift; the ability to allow easy passage is also affected by other factors such as heat. When metals are heated the energy absorbed causes thermal agitation of the molecules in the structure. This has an effect of blocking some of the electrons flowing through the material by an applied charge. This can also cause a positive feedback situation in that if high quantities of electrons are flowing due to a high electric charge driving them, then there will be collisions with atoms already thermally agitated. This will cause more agitation and therefore more heat. This up to a temperature where an equilibrium temperature occurs or the wire melts. Under controlled conditions electric fires and heating systems work by this method. The resistive quality of a material is measured in Ohms and there is a direct relationship between the electrical pressure (Volts) and the current (Amps) and the resistance. Put simply:

R (Ohms) = V (volts)/I (Amps). Below is a simplified expression of Ohm's Law.

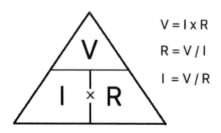

$$V = I \times R$$
$$R = V / I$$
$$I = V / R$$

Fig 12. Ohm's Law triangle

For information only, the formula for working out the current flowing along a wire of solid cylinder is:

$$nAvQ = I$$

'n' is the number of electrons, A is the cross sectional area of the wire or cylinder, v is the drift velocity and Q the charge. This formula need not be of concern to the therapist but is included to show that an important factor in determining the current is the cross sectional area A of the conductor which directly affects the current flow.

Chapter Five

MAGNETIC FIELD CONFIGURATION

To understand fully the configuration of an electromagnetic field it is necessary to again visit the basics. In therapy the shapes of the fields and how they can be directed is important when application of dynamic magnetic fields directed at specific injuries is being employed.

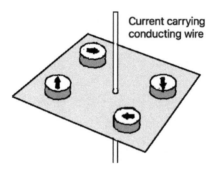

Current carrying conducting wire

Fig 13. Small compasses align to the field around a current carrying wire

A wire carrying an electric current will also have a magnetic field around it. This field will have a polarity in that it will attract or repel other magnetic fields positioned close by. The direction of the polarity can be shown by a simple arrangement as above in Fig 13 where the small compasses align themselves with the field polarity.

For clarity it is usual to illustrate the field as a 'Swiss-roll' (Fig 14) where the closeness of the loops represents the density of the field. At this stage, it does not look like the field from a bar magnet and is of little use as it is very weak.

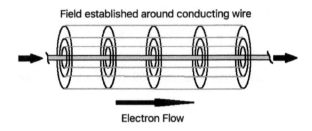

Fig 14. Field established around a current carrying wire.

It is important to note, at this early stage, that any field whether static or electromagnetic does not have a start or end but is continued as an elongated loop passing through the magnet and, as above, around the wire. The basic rule is 'where it comes from is north and where it goes to is south'. This can be applied at any position along the loop or within the field.

To increase the field strength, the wire has to be coiled with many turns. When the current is applied through the coil the small magnetic field around each loop of wire will add to that of each adjacent loop. This additive effect on the field will then begin to extend out beyond the end of the coil (see Fig 15 below).

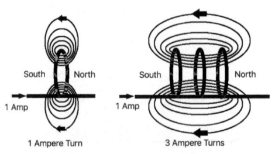

Fig 15. Additive coil loops

The comparison between the coil's magnetic field and that from a bar magnet now begins to have similar characteristics when comparing a bar magnet to an elongated coil. The field is represented in two dimensions but is three dimensional, extending like a sausage roll all around the magnet or energised coil.

The use of 'Ferrofluid' demonstrates the 3 dimensional nature of the field and a photograph of the effect on the fluid is shown in Fig 52. The field patterns illustrated could be identical to that of a permanent magnet as long as the coil has a constant flow of electrons through it. This flow of electrons within the crystal structure of a permanent magnet is due to the crystalline structure sharing electrons in an orderly direction causing an unvarying current. The field produced by them will similarly be constant and unvarying, hence static.

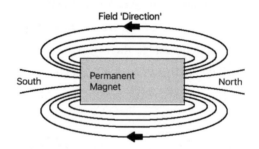

Fig 16. Permanent magnetic field pattern (Bar Magnet).

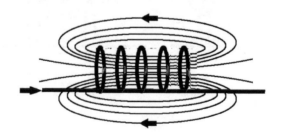

Fig 17. Field comparisons with Fig 16.

A Guide to Pulsed Magnetic Therapy

In terms of calculating the generated field, other factors now come into play to take into account all characteristics, not least of which is the length of the coil, and the number of turns. The symbol for a magnetic field is B and its density is given a unit value: Tesla. Again the full formula is given for information purposes as it applies to a static coil's generated magnetic field. The relationship of the Tesla and magnetic field densities will be discussed later in this chapter. Field densities can be calculated from the following:

$$B(Tesla) = \mu_0 \, I \, N \, / \, L$$

This formula is a simplified one and just takes into account the field density within the coil where:

μ_0 is a constant called the 'Permeability of free space' and is given a value of $4\pi \times 10^{-7}$.

I is the current in Amps

N / L is the number of turns of the coil divided by the coil length.

The diameter of the coil can be ignored as the field density will be directly proportional to the current flowing.

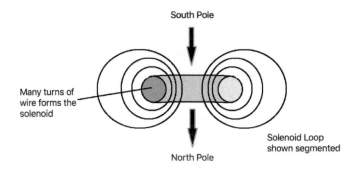

Fig 18. Segmented view of a solenoid

The name *Solenoid* is used to describe a coil of wire such as above and derives its name from the Greek meaning 'to channel'. Tightly wound coils of wire containing many (hundreds in many cases) turns, 'channel' the magnetic field produced by a common current through each individual turn of the wire, through the centre of the formed loop. The sort of solenoid that is used in pulsed magnetic therapy applicators is a tightly wound one where all of the loops of the wire are tightly gathered together.

Calculating field densities is not generally required by therapists but the terms derived are important. Tesla (B) may be found where very high strength fields are required, as in an MRI Scanner. These have field strengths of around 0.5 to 4 Tesla. In therapy most applications use fields of around 100 Gauss maximum. The Gauss Tesla relationship is 10000 to 1, or 1 Gauss = 1 / 10000 Tesla.

As previously stated measurements of field strength show a peak level to which a solenoid generates its field if it was static, but in pulsed magnetic therapy, this is never constant. It is this dynamically changing field that is required to have the necessary therapeutic effects. Therefore, the rate of change of the field has the most significance, not the field density.

The term 'mutual induction' applies to coils with oscillating or pulsed magnetism emanating from a coil causing or inducing an effect in a closely positioned metallic object or coil. The dynamic nature of the field causes it to expand and then collapse or, in some cases, completely reverse polarity. If another coil is placed in close proximity within the bounds of the electromagnetic field's expanding zone, then a voltage will be 'induced' across the second coil. If we refer to the driving coil as the primary and the one in close proximity as the secondary, the voltage is 'mutually' induced across into the secondary. The ability of coils and the amount of reactance to a changing field depends upon the characteristics of the individual coils and is give the term 'Henry' with the symbol 'L'. This reactance is given the symbol Xl and is also measured in Ohms. The significance of inductive reactance with regards to safety aspects will be covered in later chapters.

The reason why this induction occurs is that the field is a product of moving electrons. As it expands, passing through the windings of the secondary coil, (see Fig 19), the hitherto random electrons in the secondary coil will be influenced and effectively pushed along in one direction along the secondary wire by the electric charge caused by the dynamic expanding field. This movement of secondary electrons reacts against the primary ones by momentarily generating its own magnetic field in opposition to the primary inducing field. In other words, it reacts against the magnetic field causing it. This has the effect of slightly opposing the voltage as it builds up a charge across the primary coil forming the expanding field and is related to the rate of change of the field. This induced current creates a large imbalance of electrons in the secondary along the length of the coil causing a pulsating or oscillating charge across the secondary coil.

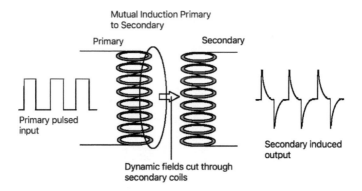

Fig 19. Mutual induction principles

The amount of charge is related directly to the number of turns in the secondary coil which the primary's field cuts through. This situation is mainly to do with electrical principles, in particular, transformers used in everything from phone chargers to all electronic gadgets; in fact virtually every electrical appliance in the world works on the same principle. It also has relevance to how dynamic magnetism works to affect changes within biological systems where tissue effectively becomes the 'secondary' to the applicator coil 'primary'. But first there is a need to understand the natural electric characteristics that exist in all biological systems.

The above discussion is an expression of Faraday's Law.

Chapter Six

THE ELECTRICAL NATURE OF BIOLOGICAL TISSUE

All functions, movements, thoughts and all of the senses of every living creature are driven by small electric charges caused by an imbalance of electrons within biological molecules. This chapter helps the reader to understand how pulsed magnetism may assist these charges to be either sustained or introduced where lacking, to aid therapeutically.

All cells of the body are driven by activity that has an electrical component or charge. This is caused by a balance of ionically charged molecules gathered near the membrane surrounding each cell: negative on the inside and positive outside. This causes a potential difference, generally of around 70 milli-Volts across the membrane. Due to the thinness of the membrane the voltage gradient is around 3 million volts per meter. The membrane consists of phospholipid bi-layers. These molecules are back to back with the tails in the centre. See Fig 20 below.

They allow the passage of water and are termed 'aquaphilic', but restrict the passage of other cationic and anionic molecules from entering or leaving except through selective channels.

The imbalance of charges between the inside and outside of the cell's membrane electrostatically establishes the voltage across the membrane. Cells rely on this electric charge between the inner and outer of the membrane which is called the 'membrane potential gradient'.

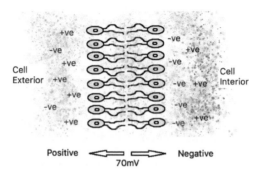

Fig 20. Cellular membrane potential

This charge, although less than a tenth of a volt, is sufficient to attract cations to the cell and, through selective membrane channels, to provide the cell with required nutrients. Also, waste products in the form of anions exit the cell attracted by the overall positive charge of the extracellular media. See Fig 20.

This cellular membrane structure is also the same for membranes surrounding axons (nerve fibres) extending from sensory receptors and neurons. This ability to allow selected anions through the membrane along all of the axons or nerves throughout the body, is significant to the transmission of nerve impulses called action potentials.

Similarly, action potentials from the brain and nociceptors and proprioceptors rely on a charge build-up at their 'axon hillocks' that reaches an electrical potential that triggers a ripple effect of sodium through the axon membrane. This 'Mexican Wave' style of inflow along the axon is also called an 'action potential'. This will be returned to in more depth later in this book.

The idea that there are other types of electrical activity was, until recently, dismissed by many as fantasy. If any medical professional suggested the existence, they could risk their reputation by suggesting that such ideas had any substance. However, recent research by American orthopaedic surgeon and scientist, Becker (1995), has established that there are indeed small direct currents around the bodies of living organisms. These are termed 'perineural currents' and are found to flow along the myelin of efferent and afferent nerves of the class A and B types. This current was identified as passing through micro apertures where each segment of myelin makes direct contact with the next. It possibly originates as a charge developed in the brain stem as positive at one side and negative at the other, and would appear to be one of the body's monitoring and feedback systems, though not fully understood at this time. It could be that the two halves of the brain may be the origin of these currents as they are known to be charged oppositely. Evidence for this is the alignment of neurons being opposite in each respective half of the brain and may be theorised as producing a charge at the brain stem. Evidence for this is discussed later in this chapter regarding a 'Trans-Cranial Stimulator'.

The existence of these direct currents has now been confirmed by experimentation and the 'Hall Effect' experiment is the one used. Methodology employs a powerful magnetic field positioned north-south across a conductor carrying an electric current, in this case being a nerve fibre. The electrons drifting at high, almost light speed, generate a small magnetic field as previously discussed. This minute field interacts with the strong static field applied across the conductor. Electrons are then forced to deviate and bunch at one side as they pass along the conductor in the area of the magnetic field. This imbalance of electrons forms an average charge that can be measured as long as the current is established and electrons flowing.

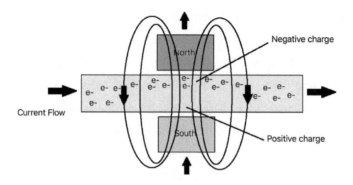

Fig 21. Hall effect experimental arrangement

Becker estimates that the current is in 'nano' or pica-amps, 10^{-9} to 10^{-12} amps respectively. This may seem very small but given that there are 6.24×10^{18} electrons in an amp then perineural currents still carry in the order of 10^6 to 10^9 electrons by volume. Perineural currents are thought to be utilised throughout the body and, in discussing the possible therapeutic effects of pulsed magnetism on tissue, their importance will be highlighted later.

Because I have now introduced the concept of electric currents within the body and will lead on to those that are not natural, then the safety aspects and limitations need to be appreciated. Where unnatural currents are forced through the body then the effects can be therapeutic or detrimental and this depends upon the amount of current entering and leaving the body. In any situation using electrical devices, there are accepted standards and levels of voltages that are considered safe. 40-50 volts DC and 35 volts AC are the recommended maximums.

In muscular tissue, contraction of the muscle involves an action potential originating from the motor cortex of the brain arriving at the motor end plate at the target muscle. This potential causes a polarising action potential that spreads across the muscle affecting the sarcoplasmic reticulum. This, in turn, causes calcium channels to open, releasing calcium into the sarcomere resulting in muscle contraction.

A Guide to Pulsed Magnetic Therapy

At levels applied to the body above 50 volts, sufficient current will pass through muscular structures to begin to cause an unnatural opening of the calcium channels in the sarcoplasmic reticulum of any muscle it may pass through. If only applied for a very short time a simple twitch may result, but muscle contraction is sustained if the current remains on. If this is at a sufficiently high level, then tetanus may occur holding the muscle rigid until the source of the current is removed. Although AC voltages may violently cause contractions as the current alternates, its level for safety is set lower at 35 volts AC. This is because the peak voltage in AC is 1.414 times greater than the average level given for AC voltages. i.e. 1.414 x 35 = 50 volts, but because of the alternating nature of AC voltage it changes between +50 volts and -50 volts, giving a total voltage difference of 100 volts. If the frequency of the AC is UK mains frequency of 50Hz, then every half cycle would stimulate muscles by reaching the critical calcium release levels so the effect would be the same as if the frequency was 100Hz. It may be that because it is alternating it could have a significant effect from the very start so that keeping below 35 volts AC is considered safe.

Although this may be not directly applicable to pulsed magnetic inductive therapy, as there is no direct electrical contact, some 'Galvanic devices' may have the potential to apply such voltages in conjunction with pulsed magnetism.

Currents induced by therapeutic pulsed electromagnetism would never normally reach sufficient levels, as discussed above, to cause contractions of muscles. However, Sheffield University Department of Medical Physics (Barker & Freeston, 2007) produced a diagnostic tool called Transcranial Magnetic Stimulator that could. It produced a very short duration peak pulse of extremely dense electromagnetism at around 14 Tesla. This causes muscles to twitch to half of the body when applied directly over the area covering the brain's motor cortex. It initiates action potentials to be sent along efferent nerves around the body resulting in the twitch.

If applied directly over a muscle that muscle, and any other adjacent to it, twitched at each pulse. Such devices are diagnostic and are not used in therapy at this time. It is interesting to note that the applicator, a small solenoid, could be pulsed with the north pole of the field being on one side and conversely the south pole on the other. This could be switched by simply turning over the applicator. When applied over the brain with the north concentration on top of the coil and south concentrated below i.e. as applied to the brain, only one side of the body twitched. If the coil was turned over exposing the brain to a concentrated north pole orientation below, the other side of the body twitched. This may be because the charges instantly induced into the brain affect neurones oriented in one way for the left side and the other for the right as part of their natural physical alignment.

It could be theorised that the left brain hemisphere, being aligned opposite to the right, may be the source of the charge driving the perineural currents. This could be due to a slight charge developed by an electrical imbalance caused by a difference in size of each cerebral hemisphere.

The next step is to understand how pulses of the magnetic field density used in therapy interact with bodily tissue. Electrons found freely within soft and hard tissue have to be explained, and how they come to be 'free'. Some understanding of these electron states and how their random nature within tissue can be influenced by dynamic magnetic fields may help in the understanding of the use of such magnetism to aid the healing process. It should be stated at this stage that there are no electrotherapies that actually heal or even speed up healing more than the body is capable of. All that may be achieved is the optimising of a body's systems to enable the repair process to start or to enhance its ability to progress at its own maximum rate.

THE BIO-ELECTRIC NATURE OF TISSUE

In the environment in which humans and animals live, the temperature is relatively high. Heat is energy and, as with all energy transfers, is in the form of vibrations. In some cases, a phenomenon known as 'Brownian Motion' can be observed where a physical manifestation occurs in fluid. When the temperature is raised to the more intense level, the more intense the vibrations. All vibrations cease at absolute zero, (-273C) or $0°K$. At a temperature of +37C, body temperature, the energetic vibrations are perfect for sustaining life without damage to tissue or internal organs. Atomic structures in all bodily systems will be exchanging electrons forming molecular structures and crystals, very much aided by heat energy. At any one time billions of electrons will be in transit between atoms, entering and leaving them randomly. The overall charge in most parts of the body will remain neutral.

An extreme example of how heat can agitate atoms to temporarily shake off some of their more loosely held outer electrons can be found in the common vacuum tube valve. It is included to demonstrate the idea and in no way relates to pulsed magnetic therapy or the temperatures involved in its application but simply included to illustrate the point of how electrons can become 'free'. See Fig 22.

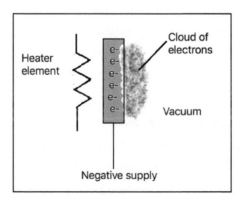

Fig 22. 'Space charge' effect

Above is a diagrammatic example of how heat can cause electrons to leave their atoms in old electronic vacuum tubes. They can occasionally be found in older radios and cathode ray tubes still used in some televisions. These devices used the 'space charge effect' to generate an electron beam aimed at the screen. This is carried out by heating a cathode so much that the electrons in it are so violently shaken that they will momentarily leave their parent atoms.

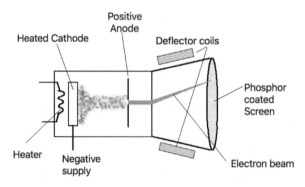

Fig 23. Space charge and the use of 'free' electrons in a simplified CRT diagram

Those near and above the surface of the cathode form a 'cloud' of electrons leaving and are then attracted back into the cathode. Because the tube interior is a vacuum, the electron cloud will exist above the cathode as long as the heat is applied physically close to the cathode. If the cathode is charged negatively then a highly positively charged anode will attract the electrons away from the cathode at high speed, and if sufficiently high, will establish a current through the vacuum. A small hole in the anode allows accelerated electrons to pass through towards the phosphor-coated screen. An electromagnetic field from coils placed at either side and over and above the beam attract and deflect it to form a 'raster'. This is a glowing line formed by the electrons colliding with the phosphor screen. Each sweep of the line is lowered vertically at high speed that in turn, with some other clever electronics, focus and make up the picture.

The bending of the beam of pure electrons by magnetic fields is an example of the 'Hall Effect'. Of course the metals used in the cathode ray tube have more easily liberated electrons and the temperatures used are far higher than in a body, but given that there are a massive number of electrons available a 'cloud' of transiting electrons could be said to exist throughout the body caused by much lower temperatures. It is these electrons that may be affected by an electromagnetically induced electric charge; this is different in application but the same in principle to the one presented by the anode in the above vacuum tube example.

A simple experiment is illustrated in the appendix and can be used to prove the fact that electrons can be made to flow through the human body. It can be carried out with the aid of a small 9 volt battery and a digital voltmeter. Get a few colleagues to hold hands in a circle, preferably an even number. The two nearest the battery each touch the terminal whilst maintaining the loop. The two people most distant then break the loop and with their spare hands grab the volt meter leads and make contact with the small metallic connectors of the leads. With the voltmeter set to 12 volts a voltage of around 8 to 9 volts will register. This shows that electrons are being 'pushed' along the right hand side loop and attracted from the left. If the volt meter is then set to amps, say $200\mu A$, then it will register a current flow. This flow is far less than required to cause muscle contraction or any sensation but, nonetheless, it safely proves the theory.

Having established that an electric current can be made to flow through the body quite safely when a small charge is applied, the next stage is to examine the charges within systems that make up the body, such as soft tissue cells and hard tissue structures and how electromagnetic induction can affect those systems.

Note: A simple electronic circuit used to effectively demonstrate the above is also included in the appendix. In the earlier chapter introducing mutual induction it was shown that if a secondary coil of wire is placed in close proximity to a primary and the primary is energized with a pulsating current through it, this will induce a current in the secondary coil that will also pulsate. This can be seen in Fig 24 below with an applicator being fed with a stream of pulses thus creating a dynamic field around it. It then has a secondary coil placed over it. The secondary coil is directly connected to an oscilloscope. It can be seen that there are a series of positive + spikes showing the induced charge in the secondary but the primary is fed with a square wave. The secondary pattern shows a series of induced pulses at the other side of the centre zero line and so pulsates negatively as the pulse is switched off. In the experimental arrangement shown there is a good match between the two coils and the secondary coil can provide a useful current to do work in some other equipment. This is typical of a charger or AC to DC converter plug-in power unit. It should be stated that in power supply devices the primary is fed with a sine wave that induces a secondary sine wave not a sharp pulse, as in the experimental case. In our case we use sharp rising and decaying pulses. In power supplies from the mains voltage, a sine wave is fed to the primary and stepped down in the secondary but still remains a sine wave before being processed.

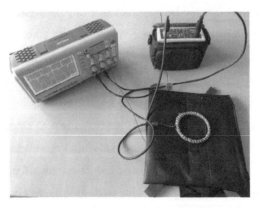

Fig 24. Induction experiment

The photo in Fig 25 of the oscilloscope screen shows the experimental exercise demonstrating the theory of secondary induction from a typical applicator into a secondary sensing coil. The square wave is the on-off base frequency being applied to the applicator, causing a pulsing magnetic field. This induces a charge in the sensing coils as seen by the spikes in the lower trace. It can also be seen that these spikes only occur when the field is either being switched on or collapsing. The slow decay back to the zero line is exponential and is a characteristic of the applicator coil.

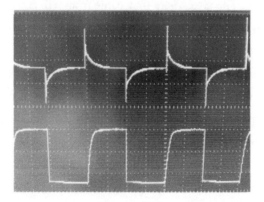

Fig 25. Oscilloscope visual representation of the induction into a secondary coil demonstration

The experimental set up to illustrate this uses the two coils that are similar to each other and as such the secondary induced charge is optimum. The flat lines show when the magnetic field is fully established (top line) or collapsed. It can be seen that no induction occurs at these times as they are effectively a static field component of the overall pulsing one. A fully 'on' field has exactly the zero inductive effect as the fully 'off' one. This also backs up the arguments against claims made for static magnet therapy.

If the concept of mutual induction is now applied to a living body, the effect will still be similar but on a very much smaller scale to the primary/secondary copper coil arrangement. The exponential decay of the very small inductive charge will be almost non-existent since the tissue would not have a reactance to the collapsing field as would a secondary coil. The random electrons within tissue will be caused to move in a specific direction as the increasing pulse of a magnetic field passes through it. This will form a charge such that the 'free' electrons will be repelled at right angles to the inducing dynamic magnetic field. The increased number of electrons pushed away from the field will form a negative charge. The area where they came from will conversely be positive. The electrons will quickly balance the charge and return to their random state once the magnetic field becomes static (see Fig 26).

When the field begins to collapse the charge is once again built up but this time in the opposite direction. We then have a sort of push-pull effect on charges that can be of great use in damaged cells. The small currents caused by electrons flowing to and from the areas where they build up are in the order of millionths of an amp (micro amps) and it is these which may have a stimulating effect on injuries.

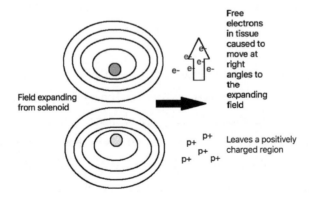

Fig 26. Build-up of charges when a dynamic field is passed through tissue

A Guide to Pulsed Magnetic Therapy

Just one pulse would in itself have little effect so the effect of pulsed magnetic therapy can be enhanced by using many pulses within an overall gated chain. The ungated chain of pulses is referred to as the 'Base Frequency'. These can range from a few pulses per second to 200. Gating in the above sense simply means switching on and off the base and therefore high frequency component.

Gating is essential as it allows an 'assimilation time' that may allow tissue time to absorb and react to the charges. This appears to have differing effects on different types of tissue. This will be discussed further in chapter 6. The shape of the pulse is very important since a faster rising pulse would momentarily induce a larger charge than a slower one. The charge therefore is related to the rate of change of the field and can be simplified to the following: -

Induced voltage (Vi) is proportional to change in magnetic field ($\delta\theta$) divided by the time taken (δt),   therefore:

$$Vi \propto \delta\theta/ \delta t$$

This represents Faraday's law stating that 'An electric field is induced in any region of space in which a magnetic field is changing with time'.

The above formula follows the fact that in the electromagnetic spectrum, in which the very low frequencies used in pulsed magnetic therapy are included, the effect on tissue is greater at very much higher frequencies. The active part of a square wave has a component much higher than the pulsing rate may suggest. The rise time of the electronics generating the pulse to be applied is in the order of nano-seconds; however, this rapid change is moderated by the coil to which it is applied, down to a rate dependent upon the characteristics of the coil but still reasonably but not dangerously high. If a coil could radiate pulsed magnetism at the frequencies that the generated pulse would match, say 1000,000,000 Hz, then biological damage would possibly occur over an extended time, causing tissue burns.

This does depend on the intensity of the radiation. It should be remembered that we are in an environment filled with high frequency radiation from both man-made and natural sources. This can be demonstrated with an AM radio where, under certain conditions, touching the aerial improves the signal. Small amounts of energy are induced on the surface area of the body and we become an extension of the radio's aerial.

With pulsed magnetic therapy applicators, the pulse generating coils cannot radiate at this very high rate because of a property called 'Inductive Reactance', as previously discussed. This simply means that it takes energy to establish a magnetic field and also means that the rate of change of the electric charge applied is opposed, offering a resistance relative to the frequency applied. It is expressed in the formula: -

$$XL = 2\pi \; FL \; (constant)$$

XL (the resistance or reactance offered) = 2π (Constant) x (Frequency) x L (inductance characteristics of the coil).

It is not necessary to delve further into the formula but it serves to reassure both practitioners and other users about the safety of therapeutic pulsed magnetic therapy with the large coils that are needed to generate the fields.

For general information: the electromagnetic spectrum covers all frequencies. Pulsed magnetic therapy, as discussed in this book, is limited to frequencies up to 200Hz. Radio frequencies start at around 20,000 (20KHz) to around 12,000,000,000 (12GHz). Light frequencies are of a much higher frequency and X-rays and gamma rays very much higher still. Radio frequencies are radiated away from their source and require antennas for this. Light, X-rays and gamma rays are radiated directly from changes in energy levels within atoms. With pulsed magnetic therapy there is no radiation as such. The energy required to establish a field remains stored in the field until the field collapses. When this occurs, the collapse back into the wire causes a charge in the opposite direction to that setting the field up. This is referred to as a 'back Emf'. Emf is short for 'Electromotive force'. The back Emf can be many hundreds of volts and the equipment driving the coil has to be designed to neutralise it otherwise damage can occur within the equipment.

The damage that radio frequencies as well as X-rays and gamma rays can do to tissue is a measure of the Relative Biological Effectiveness (rbe). The reader should not be unduly alarmed by this as it takes very concentrated radiation to cause lasting damage. Exposure to radio waves can be therapeutic under controlled conditions. It should also be noted that radiation from TV and radio stations, including satellites, induce very small voltages in the order of a few millionths of a volt in the metal aerials. Voltages far less than this would be induced in biological tissue. This should not normally present any danger.

Chapter Seven

ORIGINS OF PULSED MAGNETISM IN THERAPY

Anecdotal evidence of externally generated electrical activity aiding healing processes within the body has largely come from orthopaedics. Non-union fractures occur in up to 20% of all human long bone fractures. Where such fractures have been bilateral, some of the cases show normal healing on one side but non-union on the other. Explanations for why this should occur are sparse but research by Becker et al suggested that all injuries have an electrical component as part of the healing process. He suggested, as discussed in chapter 6, that research had proved the existence of perineural currents. It is now further suggested that these lead to the formation of 'currents of injury'. The mechanisms assisting fracture repair by pulsed electromagnetism will be discussed in depth later in the book but have relevance to these natural currents established at injury sites.

If we look at different types of injury, then whenever a trauma occurs, nerves very close to the injury site may be damaged or even severed. In the central nervous system, the mechanism for neurological repair after trauma involving severance does not generally exist because of the type of cell that forms the myelin sheath.

Oligodendrocyte cells provide most of the myelin that wraps around nerve fibres in the spinal cord. Each oligodendrocyte cell myelinates about 15 individual axon (nerve) fibres. The availability of neurolemmacytes, that are neurological repair cells, are very few and far between so there has been very little evidence of healing of the spinal cord after severance. However, in the peripheral nervous system, Schwann cells form the myelin and each individual cell myelinates just one nerve fibre. These myelin cells have the ability to repair when damaged or severed. Cuts and injuries may have some numbness to start with but feeling is quickly regained as the nerves reconnect.

The reconnection of nerves that are severed has several mechanisms. The electrical potential established at the severance site will attract neurolemmacytes through slow axonal transport. This will aid reconnection of the axon by a process of chemotactic attraction and perineural current flow leakage (currents of injury) to the distal end of the severance. Schwann cells will be stimulated to repair over the site as the axon itself repairs and reconnects.

If we apply the above logic to fractures then, where the nerves that are present at the actual trauma site are severed, several events happen. The injury itself will cause a haematoma. The formation of capillaries through possible electric and chemotactic influences will then be the cause of calcium enriched blood to flood into the area. The perineural current from the severed nerves will establish a circuit, leaking small currents across the injury site. This small current may have two other major effects:

1. It will stimulate Pluripotent-haemopoietic stem cells to de-differentiate into osteoblasts, and also....

2. Stimulate the production of bone morphogenetic proteins to cause osteoblasts to become bone.

It is important to understand the stimulative effect of micro-currents in order to gain an overall understanding of pulsed magnetic therapy that, in essence, induces micro-currents in target tissue areas. It is these small currents that have been proven in research to have a therapeutic value.

The link between perineural currents and the electrical activity around wounds was not established until the evidence for them was proven by the 'Hall Effect' but their presence was known as far back as the 1830's when Carlos Matteuci suggested that a wound or lesion was electrically active generating a charge and hence a small current across the lesion. Measurements of wound currents, now known as 'currents of injury', were proven when measured through experimentation in 1843, where about 1 microampere was measured on a human skin lesion by Dubois-Reymond.

Since then, and up to recent times, many researchers have shown the electrical nature of wounds especially electrical activity within the heart where a myocardial infarction has damaged heart muscular tissue. Although the neurological link was never really established, the currents of injury passing through and around the cardiac injury site often interfere with the normally generated polarising potential from the sino-atria node. This causes an occasional ectopic pulse and unnatural contraction of the heart. Until recently the significance of this electrical activity was never widely understood or researched.

In other areas of injury, Orthopaedic Surgeons at Hope Hospital, Salford, Manchester, would often relate to me that a non-union fracture would be helped to repair if a small current was passed across the fracture site. This was a lengthy and costly procedure in that silver terminals, in the form of pins, had to be fixed both proximally and distally directly into the bone at either side of the fracture. This treatment was therefore invasive and time consuming and the reasons for its effectiveness were not fully understood. Statistically its effectiveness is not known but anecdotal reports from the surgeons involved suggest a high success rate. Frequently it was thought simpler to place an intramedullary pin inside the bone cavity almost rigidly holding the two parts together. This then mobilised the patient and allowed them to quickly return to relative normality. The problems with this arise if, and when, the non-union does not eventually resolve and the pin has to be surgically removed, effectively initialising another injury requiring further recovery time.

It has to be noted that using the intramedullary pin method does lead to the non-union fracture healing in many cases and it may be that pressure on the fracture site, caused by mobilisation and pressures applied, in turn causes the production of piezoelectric charges directly to the injury site. The ones that do not heal would require further surgical intervention or other methods to be applied to stimulate the healing process.

The theory of perineural currents may offer an explanation into why delayed or non-resolvable fracture unions occur even in bilateral fractures. As previously discussed earlier on in this chapter, it may be that in the case of delayed union or non-resolvable union there may be other trauma in the area of the main fracture that has damaged the nerves supplying the area. If this is the case the nerves would have to reconnect, if severed, to re-establish the perineural current flow to the injury site.

It would be reasonable to assume that the delay in healing is directly dependent upon the rate of healing of the nerves. In the case of those fractures that do not eventually resolve, it may be that permanent damage to the nerves, proximal to the fracture, has occurred. A typical scenario for this is where a hip replacement or similar operation has taken place where nerves have been permanently severed (a case such as this has been reported upon in the cases in the appendix).

Methods are therefore required to allow some micro-current activity around the fracture site to stimulate healing. Gus Sarmiento, an eminent American orthopaedic surgeon and author, suggested that (during the early healing phase of a long bone fracture), some slight movement allowed between the two fracture segments may stimulate the healing process. Although he did not allude to the electrical component of healing, it is possible that piezo electric charges could be generated by such movement where the fracture segments are in contact rather than if the fracture was held stable after reduction for extended periods. It is therefore also possible that pulsed magnetic therapy may provide stimulation in the early stages of healing by providing some small inducement of currents of a similar nature to naturally occurring piezo electric ones. This sort of stimulation is applied without the need for further surgery and by electromagnetic induction directly into the injury site. The downside is that the patient would be unable to load bear as quickly as with the fitment of an intramedullary pin. However, sufficient supportive dressings allowing for gentle load bearing with slight movement at the injury site would, along with the application of Pmft, help contribute to the fracture's resolution. In chapter two the use of pulsed magnetic therapy was discussed with regard to both soft tissue lesions and fractures.

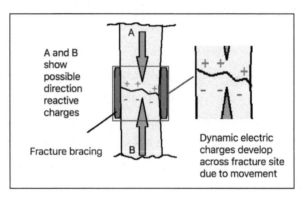

Fig 27. Fracture site piezoelectric dynamic charges

Where surgery has taken place there is no reason why starting pulsed magnetic therapy as soon as practically possible should not be used. Although the evidence for the enhancement of healing times from operative trauma has been mainly anecdotal there has never been any evidence of any negative effects. In bone where there is a natural haematoma, indicated by swelling around the fracture site, gentle palpation indicates and provides a perfect target area centred on the fracture site for treatment.

Chapter Eight

PULSED MAGNETIC THERAPY INTERACTIONS

At this stage we should now try to understand the actual processes going on in tissue under the influence of dynamic magnetic field. Again the electrons provide a possible explanation. Referring back to previous chapters on their transitory nature, caused by both heat and electrical influences, there are sufficient electrons in random transit to be able to be influenced and be of value therapeutically.

The interaction between a rapidly rising and collapsing magnetic field into tissue will cause the following effects:

1. Electrons randomly transiting between atoms will move at right angles to the pulsed magnetic field and then return to the random state. A current will be established for the short period of time whilst the 'displacement charge' exists and it is this small current that will be of use to damaged tissue to either aid the natural currents of injury or to provide a stimulating current where other trauma limits the naturally formed currents in the area.

2. Where cellular damage has occurred, this usually results in damage to the cellular membrane. This aquaphilic membrane composed of phospholipid bi-layers normally has a charge of about -70mV across it. This essential charge normally attracts anionic nutrients to the membrane. Damage will open up channels in the phospholipid bi-layer forming the membrane but then will quickly close. In this short period, cationic ions that help form the cellular charge will leak out thereby decreasing the charge. Since this charge plays an important part in the maintenance of the cell, the reduced voltage will be less effective in attracting nutrient anions up to and through selective channels in the membrane.

3. Without sufficient nutrients the cell may become less efficient in its function and eventually die. In the early stages, and providing the damage to the cell is not too great, the action of a pulse of magnetism sweeping through the cell may cause the remaining cations within the cytosol of the cell to be forced to one side of the internal cellular structure. This will then place a larger voltage at the area of bunching that will attract nutrients to that area. See Fig 28.

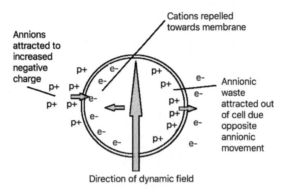

Fig 28. Possible effect on charges within a cell

The above is just a theory, probably unique to this book, but measurements by others suggest that elevated voltages exist after exposure to pulsed magnetic fields. This decreases the -70mV level to around -90mV, a level said to be 'hyperpolarised'. The above discussion may suggest the reason for this. It also stands to reason that when the magnetic field collapses a charge will again develop at right angles to the collapsing field but in the opposite direction. Cations will again be attracted to the more negative charge at the other side of the cell. This would provide a push pull action of the pulsing field beneficial in both directions. It is interesting to note that this small charge across the cellular membrane represents a voltage gradient of around 5 million volts per meter.

Another aspect of using pulsed magnetic fields to treat soft tissue injuries is that of the rate of repetition of the field applied. The rise and fall of the field is as discussed in previous chapters, but there are other considerations to be taken into account. Safety considerations are not really significant to frequencies of repetition used because of the low frequency and hence the low relative biological effectiveness (rbe).

Damage to structures at the subcellular level is only caused at very high radiative frequencies. Low frequency pulses have to be applied at steady rates. Pulsing at around 5 Hz may not have the same effect as 10 to 20 Hz but will have some effect as will be discussed shortly. The effectiveness of these low frequency pulses can be significantly increased by pulsing within a pulse. This may seem complicated but it is a simple concept if we call the low (gate) frequency pulse the 'Pulse' and the constantly generated higher frequency component the 'Base'. Remembering that the effective parts of the applied field is the rise and fall of the field, then, if during the 'on' time of the pulse component another higher frequency is imposed, the number of rise and falls is increased. This possibly causes a charge to be sustained longer and an increase in the small currents that are induced. The effectiveness is therefore likely to be increased. The 'off' time of the low frequency 'pulse' is important to allow assimilation of the charges as previously discussed.

In Fig 29 below the wave form 'A' represents the low pulse frequency. Wave form 'B' is the higher frequency 'base' component that will provide more rises and falls within the time that the waveform 'A' (pulse) is on. Waveform 'C' is the combined waveform that is applied to the applicators. The diagram is not to scale as there are many combinations of base to pulse and it is the variation of these that can be applied to different types of tissue. A typical use is where swelling occurs around an injury after the acute phase. Applying 5 pulses per second with the base of 50 Hz has an effect on capillaries that appears to be similar to adrenaline. Adrenaline will cause precapillary sphincter muscles to contract thereby increasing blood pressure. Research by Madronero (1990) has established that the application of pulsed magnetic therapy at around 5 Hz pulse had the same effect i.e. reduce swelling.

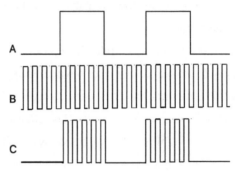

Fig 29. Generator waveform patterns

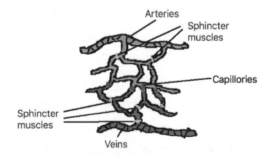

Fig 30. Precapillary sphincter muscles

The research measured brachial artery blood flow using Doppler analysis after applying Pmft over the major muscle groups in the arm. The effect lasted for up to 4 hours after 10 minutes' application. An explanation for this could be that the same electrical changes that cause the capillary contractions by adrenaline in the blood could also be mimicked by small induced charges from Pmft application.

A Guide to Pulsed Magnetic Therapy

The low pulse rate with a slightly more than equal gap between pulses gives just the right amount of electrical charge to cause the change. Conversely if pulses between 10 and 20 Hz are applied along with the 50 Hz base then this diminishes the charges that may be causing contractions and releases the sphincters, causing vaso-dilation. Normal cellular damage causes a release of neural transmitters when the damaged cell leaks out some of its cytosol as previously discussed. These are typically; bradykinins, histamine and prostaglandin. Neurological pain receptors accept one of these neurotransmitters causing it to send signals to the brain via the slow class 'C' nerves. Chronic pain is perceived as a result. Pulsed Magnetic Therapy plays a useful role in reducing the perception of this type of pain.

An understanding of how pain can be reduced lies in the fact that research has proven the change in membrane potentials after application of around 10 minutes. This change in potential is the same that has been noted on normal soft tissue cells. What sensory nerve endings have in common with all soft tissue cells is the membrane that allows selective molecules to pass through. In the case of pain receptors, they are specifically designed to accept the neural transmitter as discussed. Research has shown that application of Pmft hyperpolarises (lowers the membrane potential). The requirement to transmit an action potential from these pain sensors means that a specific charge build-up at its own 'threshold level' has to be reached that will then initiate an action potential along the nerve. If the pain sensor (called a nociceptor) is viewed as a single input neuron, then there must be a threshold mechanism at the sensor or free nerve ending that initiates an action potential in a way similar to an axon hillock threshold as found in other more complex neurons, but relatively simply controlled. This is unlike the complex decision making and multiple input neurons in the brain. The membrane potential building up at this 'axon hillock' will reach a critical level after which the action potential is triggered.

A Guide to Pulsed Magnetic Therapy

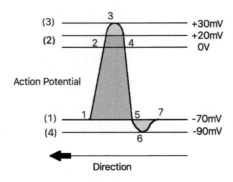

Fig 31. Normal action potential

In the above diagram the letters and numbers signify:

1. Normal quiescent or resting membrane potential.

2. Vesicle release threshold level.

3. Maximum change in membrane potential reached.

4. Hyperpolarisation level.

As shown in Fig 31, as the action potential travels along the axon it raises the membrane potential (1) from -70mV through zero volts (2). At approximately 10mV (3) a threshold level is reached. The action potential reaches its maximum of +30 mV before returning to a negative potential (4) and then through its normal resting potential (5) to a hyperpolarised level (6). It then returns back to its normal membrane potential to await the next action potential.

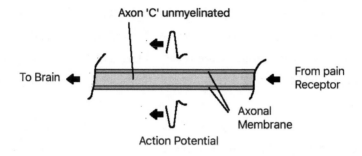

Fig 32. Axon showing an all-around mirrored single action potential

Fig 32 shows a segment of a single unmyelinated nerve transmitting a pain-initiated action potential. It originates at any number of sensory nerve endings that can transmit the chronic pain signals after an acute injury event. It then connects to chemical synapses usually at the dorsal root ganglia before entering the spinal cord. Pain receptors are very similar to the post synaptic neurone part of the synapse. See Fig 33 below.

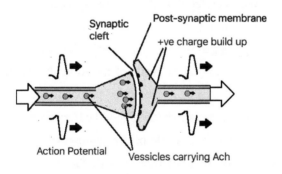

Fig 33. Chemical synapse

In the above diagram (A) is the incoming action potential. This is again shown mirrored as the inflow of NA^+ is all around the axonal membrane. (B) Shows the build-up of membrane charges that initiates an action potential from the post synaptic neuron caused by ACh receptors adjacent to the cleft. This occurs after the vesicles (C) are allowed through channels in the synaptic membrane at the cleft by the incoming action potential (A). The newly generated action potential is then transmitted (D) along to the brain or muscle depending on direction.

The sensory nerve ending (nociceptor) is similar to the post synaptic neuron but differs in that it freely opens into tissue and has receptors that allow neuro transmitters to stimulate it in the same way that ACh stimulates the post synaptic neuron. The neuro transmitters are typically histamine, bradykinin, and prostaglandin.

Applications of the effect of Pmft were measured by research where small sensory electrodes were placed inside and outside of the synaptic membranes, showing that a hyperpolarised level was reached after a 10-minute application at 200Hz applied constantly. In terms of both chemical synapses and pain sensors, this means that a larger potential (around 20mV) has to be overcome before vesicles can release acetylcholine through the synaptic membrane and across the synaptic cleft, or, in the case of pain sensors, before sufficient charges can be built up to trigger a pain-related action potential to be sent. In many cases the trigger potential is out of the reach of the stimulative neurotransmitter to achieve its activation of the pain sensor if hyperpolarised.

Research further suggests that the higher the frequency of Pmft application the more effective in achieving the hyperpolarisation state. Applying with a base of 200Hz is now most commonly used to cause the hyperpolarisation required. This frequency is limited to around 200Hz as higher frequencies applied to coils beyond this frequency will begin to suffer from inductive reactance as previous discussed. Each individual pulse applied to the applicator coils will be opposed more and more as the frequency is increased. The build-up of magnetism will begin to interfere with the next pulse in the chain, effectively flattening the waveform. This makes the application less effective. Remember it is the rise time of the pulse that the coils react to as this is of a much higher frequency than the 200Hz base frequency suggests.

Chapter Nine

ELECTRICAL ACTIVITY IN BONE

Fig 34. Scanning electron microscope image of a glass crystalline structure. Image reproduced with the permission of: Markus Heyde/Fritz Haber Institute of the MPG.

Since it was the study of orthopaedics that was fundamental to the understanding of the interaction of pulsed magnetic fields with hard tissue, it is now necessary to look at the construction of bone, its mechanical properties and such things as natural resonance for individual bones and fracture segments. Add to this the need to delve into a little electronics and the natural electric charges that can be formed within any crystal matrix of which both apatite and to some extent collagen are included.

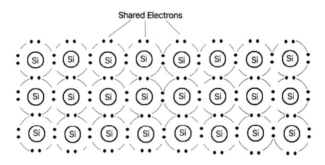

Fig 35. Silicon crystal matrix

Crystals are atoms or molecules that join with each other by sharing their outer electrons, see Fig 34, a photograph of an actual crystal matrix of thin film glass. The upper left half is the actual matrix and the lower right half is a predicted theoretical pattern overlaying it. The simplest matrix to visualise is silicon because it has four outer electrons that share with adjacent silicon atoms. Each atom has an effective stabilised valence shell by appearing to have 8 electrons in it. See Fig 35. Visualisation of this state is usually illustrated for simplicity in two dimensions but is actually three dimensional.

Although very stable, if a physical pressure is applied across the two faces of a crystal then some of the bonds momentarily break down. This allows some of the electrons to be liberated and for a while they are free forming a negative charge. The charge can only be sustained during the pressure change as the crystal is compressed. Once the pressure has ceased increasing, the electrons quickly distribute themselves until the charge they formed returns to zero. When the pressure is released, the effect on the decompressing crystal structure, as it returns to its original dimensions, is that the gaps in the crystal structure then form a positive charge that attract back the originally displaced electrons. Once the pressure is again stabilised the overall charge is again neutral. These charges are known as 'piezoelectric' and in bone are important parts of the process known as 'Wolff's Law'.

Bone, being largely constructed of collagen and apatite, is almost unique in the body systems in its ability to regenerate. The liver is the only other regenerative organ. In bone, repair of fractures, sculpturing and general maintenance all have an electrical component behind the processes. If we take a look at the structure of bone, then there are specific components in its makeup. From Figures 36 and 37, it can be seen that bone is made up of tightly packed collagen fibres forming osteons. Around each osteon, apatite crystals are bonded to the collagen by copper ions. These apatite crystals and copper ions not only add to the strength and stiffness of the bone but also are an essential part of bone maintenance. In chapter three and in other chapters, crystals were discussed and how the formation of crystals in a matrix is caused by co-valent bonding. Elements such as silicon form very stable structures with very few free electrons.

Attempting to pass a current through such structures is met with resistance in a literal sense; such structures make very good electrical resistors. If an impurity such as arsenic with either 5 electrons in the valence band or another impurity with 3 electrons, typically Indium, is introduced by doping into the crystal during formation, then there is an overall imbalance of electrons that can form the basis of current flow. In the crystal with the 5 (penta-valent) impurity. The extra electrons are not tightly bonded to their valence shell and are free to drift under external influence. This is referred to as 'N' type material because of the negative charge of the electrons.

A Guide to Pulsed Magnetic Therapy

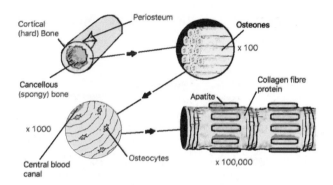

Fig 36. Cortical bone structure

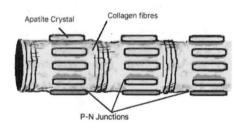

Fig 37. Collagen apatite arrangement

In the crystal with the 3 (tri-valent) impurity there is a lack of electrons within the valence shell causing 'holes' that can attract electrons into them from other atoms causing a 'hole' in their valence shell. This is then referred to as 'P' type material due to the positive effect of the holes in the structure. Since all of the atoms within the structure are neutrally balanced no overall charge exists. However, if a charge is applied across the crystal, then in the penta-valent 'doped' crystal the free electrons will drift towards the positive charge and the hole will be filled from the negative charge. This is called 'electron flow'. Similarly, in the crystal doped with the tri-valent impurity, holes will be attractive to electrons from a negative charge and more holes will appear as electrons are displaced towards the positive. This exchange of holes for electrons means that the holes effectively drift towards the negative charge. This is called 'hole' flow in electronics.

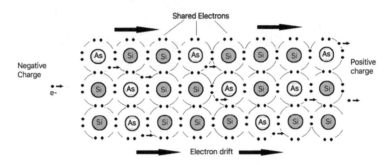

Fig 38. Silicon doped with arsenic

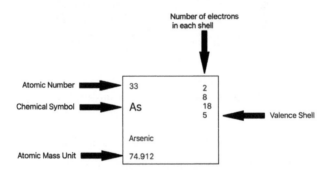

Fig 39. Periodic table representation of arsenic

Since both 'N' type crystals and 'P' type crystals can now allow a current to pass through them they are called 'semiconductors' or 'extrinsic' conductors, semi because they still offer some resistance to current flow but far less that a pure crystal.

A Guide to Pulsed Magnetic Therapy

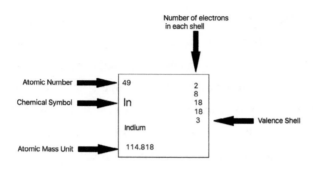

Fig 40. Periodic table representation of indium

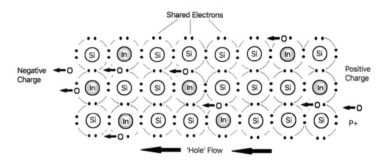

Fig 41. Silicon doped with indium.

The crystal in bone is hydroxyapatite (HA), with the chemical formula $Ca_{10}(PO_4)_6(OH)_2$. This is a large and complex crystal but has a predominately 'N' type ionic characteristic.

Collagen, although a structure with a proportion of water content, has a 'P' type characteristic in relative terms to the apatite. The fluid is ionically positive such that a biological diode is formed when these two materials are bonded together. They form a 'P-N Junction'. The significance of this can be demonstrated with a diode that will allow current to flow in one direction but not in the other. Diodes contain N and P type silicon (as shown in Fig 38 and Fig 41) that are fused together to form a P-N Junction. If a charge is applied across the junction, then electrons will easily pass from the N type material into the 'P' type. The lack of electrons in the 'P' type easily accepts the electrons donated from the 'N' type. The terms 'donor and accepter' materials apply to N and P type semiconductors in this case. If the charge is reversed, electrons cannot cross back into 'N' type material. This is because the excess of electrons in the 'N' type material will not accept them. It effectively forms a one-way device for electric current flow and in electronics forms the basis of many devices.

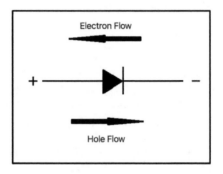

Fig 42. Diode symbol showing electron flow against the arrow

Fig 42 is the electronic representation of a diode where the arrow head points the direction of 'hole' flow. Fig 43 shows an arrangement where the P-N junction(s) are represented by diodes. The symbol for the diode is the upwards pointing arrows and bars. This is slightly misleading in the previous discussion in that the arrow is showing the 'hole' flow, with electrons flowing in the opposite direction, but is the standard electronic symbol.

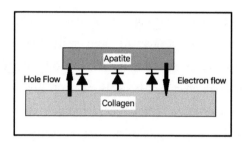

Fig 43. The P-N unction in bone modeled by diodes

Apatite is a group of phosphate minerals, usually referred to as hydroxyapatite, fluoroapatite and chlorapatite, with high concentrations of OH^-, F^- and Cl^- ions. In this case Hydroxyapatite, with the high concentration of negative ions, acts as an N type material allowing electrons to flow into the collagen that is comprised of a collection of minerals and amino acids in a positively ionic fluid. This effectively forms a relatively electron-deficient type material in comparison to the bonded apatite. This establishes a 'biological diode' allowing electrons to easily pass from the apatite to collagen but not in the reverse direction. 'Hole' flow, known as conventional flow, is the opposite of electron flow. Once the 'holes' have been effectively created by the attraction of electrons across the junction they will be filled by the abundance of electrons in the apatite. The collagen will relatively slowly dissipate the electrons but away from the biological junction and as such electrons will not be able to easily return back into the apatite. A charge will develop across the biological diode now being negative on the collagen side. The persistence of this negative charge will be an attraction for positively charged osteoblasts and osteocytes. It will also provide a stimulus for bone morphogenic proteins that are essential to the formation of bone from the cells attracted. Copper helps bond the apatite to the collagen.

In bone there are natural piezoelectric properties as found in any crystal structure. These cause charges to appear across the collagen apatite junction and, as discussed above, electrons will more easily flow from the apatite into the collagen but not the reverse. See Fig 43. It is this characteristic that plays a major part in the maintenance of bone. Bone maintains itself by the action of osteoblast/calcium deposition. The piezoelectric derived charges have several effects. They stimulate the production of bone morphogenetic proteins 2, 3 and 4. These proteins are catalysts that change the osteoblasts into bone material. The osteoblasts are cations and as such have a positive charge. Their natural attraction will be towards a negative charge.

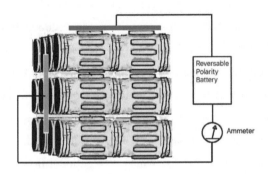

Fig 44. Bundles of collagen/apatite fibres electrically connected

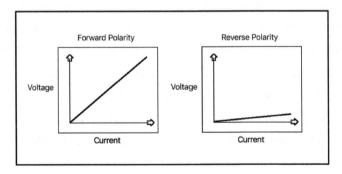

Fig 45. Forward current flow characteristics when a charge is applied and then reversed

This negative charge naturally builds up across the 'P-N' junction in areas of the most stress. Conversely small positive charges are caused when bone is under tension. This somewhat lesser charge attracts osteoclasts to the area. Osteoclasts are modified white blood cells that act to remove calcium. Bone, therefore, shapes (sculptures) itself to the stresses applied to it. This is the basis of Wolff's Law.

Wolff's law is a theory developed by the German anatomist and surgeon Julius Wolff (1836–1902). In the 19th century he suggested that where loading on a particular bone increases, typically in long bones, the bone will react and remodel itself over time to accommodate that sort of loading. He further suggested that the spongy trabecular bone undergoes adaptive changes, followed by secondary changes to the external cortical portion of the bone becoming thicker as a result.

It is interesting to note a case where an infant was born without a tibia but had a fibula in place. This was surgically repositioned and eventually took the shape of a fully functioning tibia as the child developed after being subjected to more normal developmental stresses and loading. Wolff went on to suggest that to a lesser extent the opposite is true, in that if bone is subjected to tension or reduced loading the bone will become weaker due to turnover. He reasoned that it is less metabolically costly to maintain and there is no stimulus for continued remodeling that is required to maintain bone mass.

In comparison, with the theories as to how pulsed electromagnetism helps both bones to heal, we should look at other theories that also do not mention the electrical nature of bone and its involvement with remodeling but also apply to the process of bone repair. The following is a discussion on an extract that attempts to explain Wolff's Law: other researchers have suggested that remodeling of bone in response to loading is achieved via mechano-transduction. This is described as a process through which forces or other mechanical signals cause changes. Many other papers also suggest that remodeling of bone is also achieved by mechano-transduction. A general paper along with a number of referenced articles can be found on: https://en.wikipedia.org/wiki/Wolff's_law

Mechano-transduction simply means that bone acts as a transducer. A transducer is a device that converts one form of energy to another. Since mechanical stress is accepted as the prime mover, this very much fits in with our theories of bone remodeling but the electrical component of such transduction is rarely included in such explanations. Terms such as biomechanical coupling and signal transmission also suggest that another component has to be included and that component has to be in the form of dynamic electrical charges. Also, the suggestion that static loading of a fracture or injury to bone does not achieve any effect on bone remodeling or indeed repair, and that a cyclic loading is required, fits in well with electro-mechanical principles. Both Sarmiento and Becker agree with this premise in that Sarmiento's suggestion that slight movement at a fracture site helps stimulate healing would seem to concur with Becker's piezoelectric explanations of bone-healing stimulus. Using pulsed magnetism as an inducing electric force where such cyclic loading is not practicable, as in the case of acute stages of fractures, would effectively mimic the natural transduction charges lacking at that time.

Other papers cited in the above link also omit the role that piezoelectric charges play in the process. It should now be obvious to the reader that an important statement about cyclical loading fits in exactly with the piezo induction of charges as does the signaling process of osteoblasts. Since these cells do not possess a decision-making intelligence but are statically charged, then their migration to the areas devoid of fluid has to be due to the attraction to the build-up of charges brought about by the P-N Junction between the collagen and apatite forming the bone matrix.

Wolff's law gives a good explanation to bone remodeling under normal stresses, but where a patient is sedentary and no or very little pressures are applied to the limb, as in the post-reduction phase of fractures, then we have to look to other modalities to help restore normality. The usefulness of pulsed electromagnetic therapy in this situation where a limb is suspended and not subject to the natural forces required to maintain it, is in the ability of the dynamic pulse to cause charges to be generated within bone tissue. These charges will be treated by the collagen/apatite 'P-N' junctions in the same way that natural charges are. Maintenance of bone mass is an important use of this modality, but there are other aspects of bone that need to be taken into account.

All solid structures including bone have resonance frequency. This is a frequency that will be caused to vibrate by mechanical shocks to the bone such as walking, running and general exercise. The significance of this natural characteristic is that the piezo electric effect will be maximum when the bone 'rings' at its natural frequency because this will allow maximum stresses to be applied. Natural resonant frequencies depend on several factors: the size of the bone, its density and the surrounding environment such as supportive muscular soft tissue. Research by ourselves at the Department of Orthopaedic Mechanics at the University of Salford found that a peak in-vivo resonance in human long bones occurred in a broad range of 100 to 140Hz. See Fig 46 below.

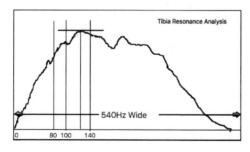

Fig 46. In-vivo bone resonance response to an electro-mechanical stimulus

The method of mechanically stimulating the bone at its resonance was to use a specially designed electronic impacting device applied to the tibial tuberosity (see Fig 48). The impactor was driven by another also specially designed electronic device that applied a series of short duration high-powered mechanical pulses. These were applied at 25 times per second.

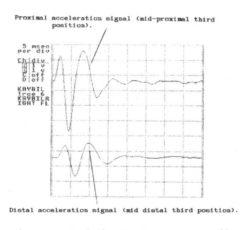

Fig 47. Actual trace typical of an in-vivo response of bone 'ringing' in a normal tibia.

Transducers mounted mid-shaft over the tibial crest recorded the responses of the bone and from these transducers a sampled damped oscillation, (see Fig 47), at the natural resonant frequency was produced. The damped oscillation lasted a maximum of 3 peaks.

Fig 47 above illustrates two traces of the output of accelerometers. The slight displacement between the two signals along with the reduction in amplitude is a function of speed of the shock wave and the attenuation along the bone.

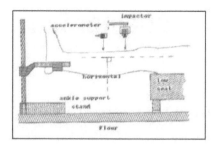

Fig 48. Experimental arrangement for bone resonance (single accelerometer)

Scanning the bone with a spectrum sweep, using the same equipment, of 0 to 500Hz confirmed the approximate peak resonance previously deduced from the damped oscillation trace. It should be noted that our initial experiments were carried out on ourselves and other volunteers, usually doctors or students. The same characteristics were achieved for us all and Fig 46 generalizes these results.

When pulsed magnetic therapy is applied to bone, its effect is not only the induction of small charges but also that these charges will momentarily deform the bone. A characteristic of all crystalline structures is that if an electric charge is applied across the face of the crystal it will momentarily deform and then ring a damped oscillation until again stable. A pulse of magnetism applied to a bone at or near the resonance should optimize the effect by not only inducing a charge in the bone but further causing the bone to microscopically deform and ring, generating its own piezoelectric charge. It is for this reason that 50Hz pulses applied to bone optimizes the effect in that the pulses are sufficiently spaced to allow a natural resonant damped oscillation of 140-160Hz to occur. For the veterinarian or therapist, it is important to understand these concepts and to justify the frequencies used in pulsed magnetic therapy when applied to orthopaedic problems.

Chapter Ten

APPLICATION OF PULSED MAGNETIC THERAPY

The generation of pulsed magnetic fields has been discussed and the term 'solenoid' introduced in chapter 5. In normal situations where application can be in a clinic, home, stable or in a field, the application methods need to be studied to achieve maximum benefits.

Applicators are constructed using tightly bound coils (solenoids). The dimensions of these applicators are important to enable the pulsating fields to generate charges in the target area. Some applicators have multiple solenoids that can interfere with adjacent ones. This can be desirable or problematic depending upon the size and position of a specific injury. Treating each solenoid as an individual field generator is a good way to start and these can be modelled using static magnets to model the field interaction and shape.

Static magnets can either attract or repel each other. The same applies to pulsating magnetic fields. The most common form of applicator is the wrap type. This consists of two coils (solenoids) built into a wraparound structure. The coils are usually wound so that when one coil is placed close together with the other, the resulting effect is to have a single coil generating almost double the peak intensity of magnetic fields. This requires them to be wound in the same orientation and supplied with the same current. If the two are applied in the same plane across a limb, then provided that they fully magnetically complement themselves, a fairly even field across the injury site can be established. Such an effect is called the 'Helmholtz Effect' provided the distance between the two coils is within the diameter of each coil. See Fig 49. This is a useful configuration when treating lower limb joint and other orthopaedic long bone injuries.

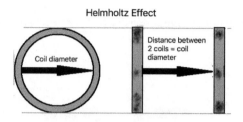

Fig 49. Helmholtz coil arrangement

Other methods of using a wraparound applicator whose field is complementary (Fig 50), is to place it flat over a specific area where a known injury site has occurred.

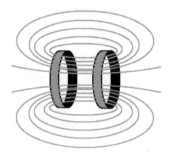

Fig 50. Fully complementing coil fields

When the applicator is opened out so that the coils lay next to each other, the fields still complement each other, as seen in Fig 51, showing the generalised fields pulsing from the coils that are supplied from a common source and oriented on a flat plane. The field densities are represented by:

'A' is a null point where minimum field exists as it is directed upwards and around across to join up with the adjacent and still complementary field from each solenoid.

'B' is where the field is more flat and horizontal. It has a relatively high density and covers a wide area.

'C' has a narrower but higher density and is more vertically oriented.

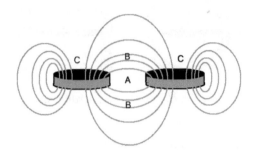

Fig 51. Complementary polarity: coils side by side

At this point it should be noted that the diagram represents more of a 2-dimensional view of the field, but it is 3-dimensional, extending all around the coil arrangement. (See photo in Fig 52.) This is the pattern formed around the end of a single disc magnet to illustrate the field from a solenoid. Since pulsed magnetic fields are constantly changing the shape of the field, modelling such as this can only be carried out with a static field. The spikes that form the patterns are created because the fluid comprises minute iron particles suspended in an oil that align themselves to the field. The spikes point the direction of the field and the density of the spikes indicates the field strength. This end-on photo also shows the 3- dimensional natures of all magnetic fields as they loop around the magnet.

The extent to which a field can reach and therefore be effective depends upon many factors. These include:

1. Coil physical dimensions
2. Number of turns that make up the coil
3. Current passing through the coil, and
4. Proximity of the applicator to the target tissue.

Coil physical dimensions should be large enough to cover an injury site with sufficient pulsed field density. Thick and heavy wire will produce a good field but at the cost of the amount of current required to produce the field and also the weight of the applicator.

Fig 52. Ferrofluid with pattern (copyright D C Somerville)

This affects the number of turns required in the coil. Assuming the dimensions, weight and electrical loading are acceptable, the next consideration has to be the proximity of the applicator to the target tissue.

The treatment of superficial muscular injuries does not present any real difficulties except where larger muscles extend deeper in the body. Typical of these are the gluteal muscles. For an injury at depths of several centimetres from the surface the applicator may require a stronger field. In the case of a portable pulsed magnetic therapy device, this can present problems in that to produce a stronger field would require an increase in current through the coil(s). This is not as simple to achieve because doubling the current increases the heat generated in the coil by four times. Since the heat is a function of power given in watts, the energy lost is given by the *formula $I^2R = P(Watts)$*. In simple terms the higher the current 'I' the greater, by the square of the current the power consumed and would be difficult to sustain from a small battery-powered device for very long. Also this would overheat the coils for devices having greater power.

This problem is not insurmountable as design and alignment of the coils themselves can increase the intensity of the magnetic field. This is achieved by having more loops in the coil to have an additive effect producing a stronger field. However, if a single tight solenoid is used with more loops in the coil the intensity of the field is confined to the close proximity of the coil as shown below in Fig 53. The intensity is quickly reduced as the coil is placed even a short distance from the target tissue. The field intensity is greatest in the centre of the coil, as shown, but at points A and B the field is very weak, even close in. This makes a single solenoid only useful for superficial treatments.

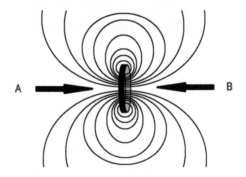

Fig 53. Single coil field pattern (viewed end on would be similar in shape to the ferrofluid model)

The problem of getting the pulsing field to reach to deeper injuries, such as those found in the sacroiliac area (SA joint) in horses, requires applicators that will extend the pulsed field with sufficient density to penetrate the SA. The total depth needed to be penetrated is dependent on the size of the animal but could be 10 - 15cm below the skin surface. A method that can overcome this lack of field density at required distances from the coils is to use several coils of differing diameters. These are built concentrically so that when energised, the fields from all of the coils are directed through the innermost one.

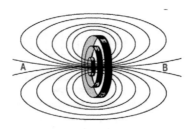

Fig 54. Multiple concentric coil field

Each individual solenoid acts in the same way as individual loops of a coil. A common field is then established around the multiple arrangements. It can be seen from Fig 54 that the multiple coil arrangement extends the field well beyond that from a single solenoid. The points A and B are now in an area of much higher field intensity.

Orientation of individual applicators when applied alongside other applicators needs to be considered, when applying treatment to deep muscles. If the applicators are applied from a single source, see Fig 55, where pulse waveforms are synchronised, then the fields generated either complement or repel.

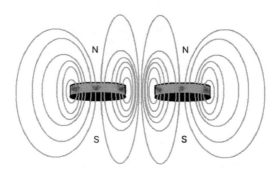

Fig 55. Side by side coils with opposing fields

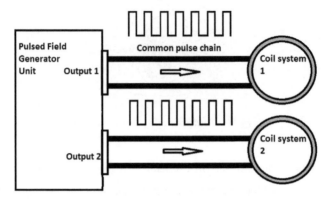

Fig 56. Individual coil connections

Applying the coils oriented correctly to gain optimum exposure to injury sites can be achieved by careful positioning of the applicators.

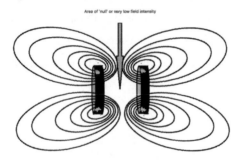

Fig 57. Repelling fields coil formation

Fig 57 above shows the arrangement where the pulse rate of the two applicators are synchronized and placed side by side. The arrow points to a 'null' point where very little field exists because of the repelling effect. Any injured tissue placed under this arrangement would have a field on each side of the target but very little over it. The next illustration is a copy of Fig 51. This could be where a wraparound type applicator is applied as a flat one to cover a larger area. A typical wrap type applicator opened up against the target area would achieve this pattern as long as the coils were complementary.

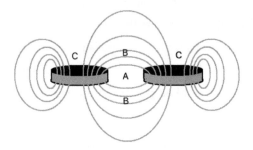

Fig 58. Repeats Fig 51.

Any injury placed in positions B would be subjected to a strong field provided the applicators are placed either side of the focal point. This method allows for treatment of a large area.

Bilateral treatment using complementary coils can provide even fields between the coils, provided that the Helmholtz radius is not exceeded but it is more likely that this will not be the case. Where there are bilateral withers injuries on a horse, two coils suspended at either side and in complemetary orientation may well provide an even field across the body. Treatment of bilateral stifle injuries are too wide for this formation so the orientation is not an issue. Two individual applicators can be placed directly over each stifle.

Where two generator units are used, both of the same type coupled to identical applicators, a condition of the fields call 'heterodyning' can arise. This simply means that the two units may have identical settings of both frequency and base so that they may add or subtract from each other, both cancelling and adding at the small 'difference' frequency. This is because it is almost impossible to achieve synchronous unless electronic coupling between the two units is achieved. To date no manufacturer has seen the need to couple more than one unit to another. See Fig 59.

'A' represents the pulse chain applied to one of the applicators. 'B' is fed to a closely adjacent applicator. The wave pattern 'C' now represents the field intensity applied to the areas where the fields interact. Although not illustrated, what would confuse the pattern even more is if either or both pulse chains, that represent base frequencies, were to be pulsed. The frequency specific qualties of the pulsating fields would be greatly diminished in the overlap.

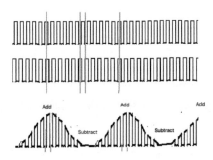

Fig 59. 'Heterodyning' effect of adjacent coils where near same frequencies are applied.

In this chapter we have seen some of the types of field patterns around single or multiple coil arrangements and the importance of positioning with respect to target tissue. This is not an exhaustive account but serves to illustrate how a little thought to the positioning of applicators can enhance their effect over injury sites.

Chapter Eleven

POSSIBLE PULSED ELECTROMAGNETIC STIMULATIVE EFFECTS ON DNA SYNTHESIS.

The electrostatic and chemical attractions involved in DNA formation and the production of proteins is both amazing and intriguing in how it occurs and is sustained throughout life. The osteogenesis of bone where fractures occur is an example of the use of DNA within immature erythrocyte blood cells before they become anucleate. This simply means red blood cells that have not achieved their bi-concave disc shape through maturity following the ejection of the nucleus. The DNA within them at this stage can still be stimulated to dedifferentiate into other forms of tissue under certain conditions. Also rapid build-up of charges in bones stimulate the production of specific proteins. Bone Morphogenic Proteins (BMP) are required for the formation of new bone from osteoblasts attracted to the area by the same charges.

Pulsing magnetic fields applied through bone will induce small charges, the magnitudes of the charge depending on the rate of change of the field (see chapter two). How these interractions actually affect DNA changes is speculative but may be a product of 'eddy' currents affecting the molecular structures required as building blocks to be more evenly spread around the area. To grasp this a look at DNA structure and divisions to the production of proteins is required. The term 'eddy currents' refers to small circling currents caused by a disturbance similar to those caused in water by oars or objects disturbing current flow. In every day situations involving pulsed magnetism they can be found creating heat in pans from induction hobs and to a very much larger extent in steel smelters. In tissue these currents would be too low to involve any measurable heat but may create a disturbance in body fluids.

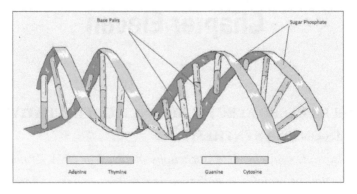

Fig 60. Segment of DNA

DNA (Dioxy-ribonuclear acid) is a double helix structure found in the nucleus of every living cell. In humans, if the strands of DNA from every cell were to be laid out end to end in straight lines, the distance along would be several times the distance from the earth to the sun, which is in the region of 150,000,000 km or 92,000,000 miles.

The illustrated double helix in Fig 60 forms just a minute section of a strand of DNA. The sugar phosphate forms the actual helix shape linking together base pairs. These base pairs are molecules that in general only interact and join with specific base pairs called nucleotides. Adenine always pairs with Thymine and Guanine with Cytosine. These nucleotides chemically link on to the sugar phosphate by interaction with specific molecules in the phosphate chain. Although a complex process, it is the interaction of charges in specific combinations that attract exactly equal and opposite sequences of molecules. Electrostatic attraction is therefore the binding force that holds biological matter together down to the level of DNA and within molecular structures.

Cells that contain a nucleus are known as eukaryotic cells and are capable of replication or, as it is more commonly known, mitosis. Again it is an interaction of charges within the nucleus that cause an invasion of microtubules that attract the DNA strands causing them to divide into two. These two halves of the strands then attract base pairs from within the cytosol in the exact sequence of the original. These then form daughter cells that will in themselves eventually go through mitosis. Further reading on these processes is recommended but the limited information here is given to show the electrical nature of growth and cellular reproductive process that may be enhanced by the influence of pulsed magnetism.

In a similar way protein production, that is essential to the repair processes in both hard and soft tissue, needs a basic understanding to again appreciate the electrostatic processes involved. In bone, charges build up in areas of stress such that a predominantly negative charge will accumulate where compressive forces are present. This will trigger biosynthesis of morphogenetic proteins that act as catalysts to form osteoblasts from osteoprogenitor cells by metamorphosis. Osteoblasts are positively charged and have the capacity to form bone. Osteoblasts form from osteocytes found within the lacunae of bones. The morphogenetic proteins are produced from DNA structures where a process similar to mitosis occurs but with essential differences.

DNA cannot form proteins directly and so has to undergo a process known as transcription.

The process illustrated in Fig 61 below shows Gene Expression in that a segment of the DNA strand unravels (A). Free RNA (D) called Ribonucleic Acid (RNA), matches with the correct pairing sequence on the unravelled DNA strand until a Uracil molecule pairs with Adenosine. This severs the sequence. B shows where the DNA regains its normal double helix shape and C the direction of the mRNA (m stands for 'messenger') strand leaving the DNA structure. This mRNA strand then leaves the nucleus and enters the endoplasmic reticulum (ER) within the cell.

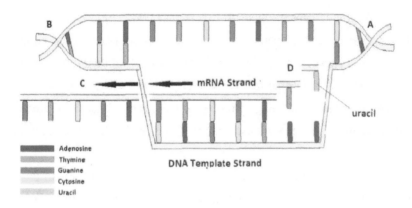

Fig 61. Transcription of DNA (Ribonucleic Acid)

The codes, in sets of three, are called codons. Ribosomes move along the mRNA codon chain translating it into polypeptides within the ER. This is carried out by transmitter RNA (tRNA) complementary pairing with the mRNA. The tRNA molecules carry their own specific amino acids. These join neighbouring amino acids, by what is known as a condensation reaction, forming the polypeptide chain and hence the protein.

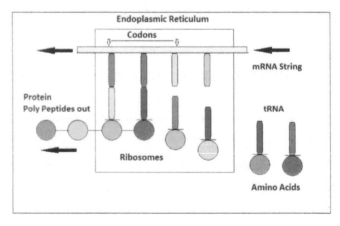

Fig 62. Protein production process

The above sequence (Fig. 62) has been somewhat simplified and condensed but serves to show that electrostatic attraction plays the major part in the attaching and bonding of the various parts of the process, especially since DNA itself is known to have a specific electrostatic overall polarity. Charges induced by pulses of magnetism around cells undergoing mitosis or in the process of producing essential proteins would effectively stir by possibly causing 'eddy current' swirling charges in the cytosol of the cells that contain statically charged tRNA and amino acids. This may allow for a more even distribution of the major acids and elements and optimise the efficiency and hence the speed of the processes.

All processes discussed come down to the balance of electrons within the complex structure found within the body. A simple analogy would be to think of the attraction and repulsion as a series of coded charges represented by + and − i.e.

$$+ + - - - + - + +$$

presented at the end of a specific molecule would easily electrostatically bond with a:

$$- - + + + - + - -$$

presented pattern from another molecule. This may be a simplistic form of logic but it is obvious to see that the electron balance code has to be exact to match and only one charge difference or out of sequence on either molecule would cause repulsion. This is similar to a complex jigsaw piece that is unique, only able to match a complementary pattern.

Since magnetism is the product of a flow of electrons all electrons within the structures of the body would to some extent be influenced by pulsed electromagnetism and it is within this context of the effect on free electrons that the therapeutic value is derived. The charges, though minute, induced by Pmft with the free electrons, would be able to stimulate movement and the rotation of molecules to allow coded alignments more efficiently.

Chapter Twelve

IRON IN BLOOD AND GENERAL DISCUSSION

Much of this book is based on facts, theory and some speculation about a subject that some clinicians find difficult to accept. Veterinary Surgeons have possibly led the way in adopting pulsed magnetic therapy into their practices, after seeing for themselves the positive results for a variety of conditions by their therapist's use of it. Pulsed Magnetic Therapy is now widely used by veterinary therapists. As veterinary physiotherapy training, with more formalised and accredited courses now being run, pulsed magnetism as an electrotherapy treatment modality is now formally taught in some institutions but not all. However, there are still many in the caring professions, both veterinary and medical, that consider the main interactive organ to magnetism is that of blood; this is because of misconceptions about its iron content.

There is still confusion in the wider public about 'magnet therapy'. In this book I have tried to distance pulsed magnetism from that of 'static magnets therapy', as they are as different as chalk and cheese as far as therapy is concerned. Since the word magnetism appears in both, even students sometimes have difficulty differentiating between them. Blood flow is claimed to have magnetic properties according to the static magnet proponents. Somehow they believe that strapping a magnet on the wrist in the form of a watch-style device, or over injuries, 'draws' blood to the area due to red blood cells having iron in them. I have even read adverts for these devices that claim that blood cells align themselves and even somehow take up more oxygen simply by flowing through a static magnetic field. I'm sure a good salesman could make it sound very plausible and the multi-million-dollar industry around static devices attests to their successful salesmanship. The truth is, however, somewhat different.

Fig 63. Bi-concave shaped red blood cells

Blood is an amazing organ of the body. It is indeed the life force that sustains all other organs and processes. Approximately two million red blood cells are formed every second in a human and conversely two million degrade. Red blood cells are also known as erythrocytes. The part of blood that magnet therapists latch upon is that of iron found within haemoglobin. This gives blood its characteristic red colour in appearance. There are around 280,000,000 haemoglobin molecules in every individual red blood cell. Males have around 5,600,000 red blood cells and females 4,700,000 per cu mm. The sheer number of red blood cell in the body is many, many billions and the number of haemoglobin molecules many orders greater. So the amount of iron is seemingly very high given that there are 4 ionic iron atoms embedded within each of 4 polypeptide chains forming each molecule.

In the following diagram (Fig 64.) I have represented the 4 polypeptide chains by a series of coloured and linked circles. A different colour represents a different chain. The iron ions, called 'haems', are set within the centre of each chain and are represented by bright red circles. It can be seen that the iron ions called 'haems' are not in any way directly connected to each other.

In chapter two it was discussed that electrons flowing in an orderly manner create a magnetic field in an iron matrix. This field can interact with adjacent magnetic fields. In haemoglobin molecules, there are no iron matrix structures that could sustain a flow of electrons sufficient to cause the formation of an interactive magnetic field. Haems (ionic iron) are, therefore, not generally affected by external static magnetic fields. Take the case of MRI scanners with a field of 0.5 to 4 Tesla which works by subjecting target tissue to this extremely strong magnetic field (remember that 1 Tesla = 10,000 Gauss). This very dense magnetism causes randomly aligned hydrogen H_2 molecules in tissue, to order themselves with the north-south orientation of the field.

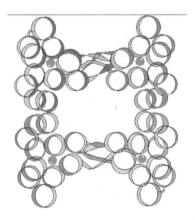

Fig 64. Haemoglobin molecule

(Hydrogen molecules are usually in pairs sharing their electrons so that each hydrogen molecule has an elongated shape. These molecules normally have no specific alignment). A directed pulse of radio frequency energy causes some of the hydrogen molecules to flip orientation. At the end of each pulse, hydrogen molecules again flip to realign, in doing so, releasing a pulse of electromagnetic energy themselves. It is these electromagnetic pulses that are detected and processed to produce a visual image. When the patient is removed from the scanner there is no affect that can be detected in either blood or the tissue due to being exposed to such a high density static field. It would possibly be a death sentence if blood was attracted to the exposed area, as suggested by the static magnet lobby, when under an investigation using MRI scanners. Blood would be drained from the rest of the body by the very intense field with fatal consequences.

It is a fact that iron, being a larger atom, is slightly diamagnetic and this is sometimes latched onto by static magnet therapy proponents, but it is microscopic in the extreme and also random within blood flow. The haem is a charged ion and has a deficiency of electrons therefore less able to individually align to any external magnetic influence. It has been calculated in an undated internet article by David W Ramey DVM that blood would be caused to deviate by roughly one tenth or less of the diameter of a carbon atom whilst flowing through a 250 gauss static magnetic field. This is far less than the natural movement caused by thermal agitation from body heat. Most magnets applied to the body in the form of watch-type devices or pendants have a very weak field akin to that found on fridge magnets.

Terms like 'rare earth' are used in promotion literature as if to ascribe some magical properties, but simply refers to elements made up of Neodymium, Iron and Boron (NdFeB). These elements are used to make strong permanent magnets. Usually these are used in industry but occasionally found in some static magnetic applicators. They are useful when used with pulsed magnetic therapy applicators simply in that they will physically vibrate, caused by the intermittent attraction of the pulsed generated field when placed within that pulsating field, thus allowing the user to check that the applicator is functioning. This is a simple example of the electric motor principle, and demonstrates pulsed field integrity for what is, in the main part, a sensationless modality. Other than their use as test magnets, they have no value in therapy.

One particular manufacturer markets their device claiming that the arrangement of the magnets sharply reverses the field, thus affecting electrons suddenly encountering it. The random nature and sheer volume of free electrons means that if such claims were true then for every electron diverted in one direction another would be diverted in the opposite, thus the net effect would be zero. Also if two small magnets were fixed so that the two opposing poles were physically forced together then the flip in magnetic fields would produce a null point as the repulsion affects the field density around the area of the junction between the two. The gradient of field polarity change would not be instant so rapid effects on electrons would not occur. It is also not clear as to the benefits of electron diversion if the claims were true and is an example of pseudoscience being used to sell a product without any empirical research evidence offered.

In some of my previous articles I have made a suggestion for discussion that a very strong permanent magnetic field may interact with tissue due to the relative motion of tissue to the applied magnet. Suggested mechanisms for such interaction were molecular vibration due to heat. Such vibrations are totally random, not aligned, and incredibly small. If any therapeutic charges were formed they would effectively cancel out and be impossible to detect.

The second interactive vibration that I suggested was due to heart beats. Pulsating arteries, and to a lesser extent veins, would cause tissue to slightly move as it absorbs the beat. The two problems with this is that any magnet placed on or near any pulsing tissue would also be caused to move with this tissue. Relative movement between magnet and tissue would again be very small. The second problem is that, as has been discussed in previous chapters, the rate of field change has to be relatively high to induce any appreciable charge in tissue. The slow rate of rise and fall of tissue would cause negligible charges with any tissue subjected to a static field.

The third mechanism that I considered was that of relative movement of a loosely held magnet over tissue, as in a pendant or wrist band. Again, as alluded to in the previous paragraph, relative movement is small and again the rate of interaction too little in itself to have any affect. Credible peer reviewed research is lacking and where such limited research has been carried out (see references of a sample of papers below) sham devices seem to have equal effect to real ones. Since from simple physics that energy has to be put into a system before it can be taken out, static magnet therapy has to be classed as pseudo-scientific verging on the metaphysical for those who believe in it. I would suggest that the packaging of such devices provides more therapy than the embedded magnets could ever do. This is simply by providing a thermally insulated area under the magnetic device.

The other aspect of a static magnet therapy is that of attempting to mimic frequency. Attempts have been made to use such magnets in rotating magnetic columns to provide a varying and therefore dynamic magnetic field. One such device is referred to as a 'wand' and the claims by the makers for it were quite unacceptable. Such a device would be an improvement on fixed static applicators but not specific enough to be able to be a targeted application. Also the alternating field would be sinusoidal and very low. Manufacturers of magnet devices tend to make claims referring to the ability of their devices to cure and improve many ailments. One made by a wand device maker claims it had cured cancer!! They may say that scientific research backs up their claims but there is never any empirical research that can be quoted.

It is my hope that this book has offered a scientific approach to this modality, opening the eyes of some. Also, that after reading it, a different point of view can be had of the usefulness of this natural phenomenon when scientifically applied. Also hopefully some of the misconceptions and myths have been laid bare.

Some interesting reading on the subject of static magnet therapy can be found in the following papers:

1. Brody, J. 2000. Less pain: Is it in the magnets or in the mind? *New York Times*, November 28: F9.
2. Weintraub, M. 1999. Magnetic bio-stimulation in painful diabetic peripheral neuropathy: A novel intervention-a randomized, double-placebo crossover study. *American Journal of Pain Management* 9: 8-17.
3. Finegold, L., and Flamm, B.L. 2006. Magnet therapy: Extraordinary claims, but no proved benefits. *British Medical Journal* 332: 4.

And finally..........

There are among those who read the text some who may disagree with some of my theories and statements about various aspects of therapeutic magnetism. I make no apologies as I have tried to apply scientific principles based on my own physics, chemistry and electronic engineering background, as well as the clinical research that I was involved in at Salford University for my doctorate. Such is the nature of research that peer-related critical analysis is expected. However, to such individuals I would suggest another book putting their own theories forward, as relatively little is written on this subject and the basis for future research is wide open.

Appendix 1

CASE HISTORIES

Introduction

The proof of its efficacy of pulsed magnetic therapy lies in the practical application and noted results. This appendix highlights some notable case histories in mainly human use. It is also interesting to note that many of these human cases were accompanied by an understandable degree of scepticism, especially as some of the subjects treated were from within the medical profession. In some instances, they have regarded pulsed magnetic therapy as a last resort for seemingly unresolvable cases. In each case I was approached by either the patient, orthopaedic surgeon or consultant involved in the case. Where the patient has approached without the approval of the medical specialist, I have directed them to seek approval before commencement of treatment.

I have added a fairly recent veterinary case as Case History Nine due to its unusual circumstances and outcome. The condition of the injury at the outset and eventual outcome was verified by veterinary surgeons, the latter through an autopsy. This was required because the animal died due to different circumstances to that which caused the original injury.

Although I have limited the number of cases reported there are many more (hundreds) of anecdotal reports going back over 20 years. These have all had positive outcomes and there has never, in my experience, been a negative response indicated or reported. Patient anonymity has to be respected so the cases are generalised to the basic information about the background and conditions both prior to and post treatment and the subsequent outcome.

All human patients listed below, except one, were treated with the full knowledge and supervision of the consultants involved and carried out both privately and within the NHS. These cases were considered experimental and no financial charges were made to either the patient or the NHS. The equipment was loaned, in most cases, free of charge. It seemed to be the medical consensus of opinion that such treatments are more psychological and as such could do no harm. The ethical aspects were not considered to be necessary since no placebo- controlled trial could be carried out with individual cases.

Orthopaedic injuries provide the most reportable and recordable cases. Radiographs provide good before and after comparisons of progress. It is within this field that pulsed magnetic therapy had initially gained its reputation. The orthopaedic cases following are samples cases that are typical of many reported and advised upon.

All but one of the cases recorded below have been strictly kept to human cases since direct communication with the patient provides good feedback that can be backed up by medical opinions. Its use with animals is widespread and the number of cases numerous but it is very hard to vigorously check each case as most are reported anecdotally. This is not to suggest that these reports are unreliable, quite the contrary. The vast volume of successful outcomes reported from veterinary surgeons and veterinary physiotherapists must bear witness to the efficacy of pulsed magnetic therapy as a treatment modality. In all cases double blind placebo controlled research with acute injuries is ethically questionable. These tend to be restricted to chronic cases in humans where statistical analysis can be applied based on a large number of subjects. It is my contention that in severe cases, the need to provide relief and stimulation of natural healing processes overrides anything else.

Case Study 1 Human

Patient (M). Age 60. Occupation: Consultant Surgeon.

Symptoms: non-union # to mid-shaft femur.

Time post injury until Pmft: approx. 4 Years.

Other complications: full hip replacement on injured leg prior to #.

Treatment up to Pmft: plated, pinned and wired across #.

Prognosis: poor. This patient had fractured his femur 4 years before using Pmft. Operations to pin, graft and wire the fracture had had little effect.

Referred for treatment using Pmft. The suggested regime was 50Hz/constant with 3 x 20 minute treatments across # daily. Progress was recorded by radiographs from onset of treatment.

Radiograph 1 showing fracture to femur, plate and prosthetic implant

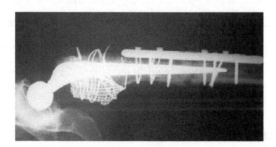

Radiograph 2 taken just post op showing new prosthesis wiring and plating. A state of non-union remained for some considerable time after the operation

Radiograph 3 taken after 11 months of regular treatment with Pmft showing almost complete bridging of the fracture.

The above radiographs were taken from a series of one per month over a 12-month period and reproduced with the permission of the patient.

Progress: 7 weeks suggested evidence of bridging.

15 weeks: firm evidence of bridging

Continued growth up to 50 weeks when declared 95% bridged. Patient returned to normal life and duties.

Comment:

This case is typical of fractures where there is some neurological damage. The very fact of having a replacement hip would sever many nerves linking the femur to the central nervous system. This would appear to back up the theories of peri-neural currents playing a part in normal healing but being absent in this case.

Case Study 2 Human

Patient (M). Age 50-60. Occupation: University Professor.

Symptoms: non-union # to mid-shaft femur.

Time post injury until Pmft: approx. 1 Year

Other complications: none known

Prior treatment: reduction and cast

Prognosis: none stated.

Referred for treatment using Pmft. The suggested regime was 50Hz/constant with 3 x 20 minute treatments across # daily.

Progress was recorded and verbally reported after each clinic visit.

Progress: 1st visit post onset of Pmft: evidence of bridging.

Next report after 6 months: firm evidence of bridging to 80%

Bridging was observed to continue up to 52 weeks when declared fully united. Patient returned to normal life and activities.

Comment

This patient was not a medical academic but was initially referred by his brother-in-law who was a retired professor of pathology. After ensuring that he had full support from his own specialist he showed a great deal of scepticism, as did his wife, about pulsed magnetic therapy treatment and, with some reluctance, began to follow the suggested regime. Both of their attitudes changed very quickly as radiographs showed evidence of bridging from relatively early after commencement of treatment. It is interesting to note that they recently approached me about another injury. I suggested that they were within a time frame well inside of that for the declaration of a non-union fracture. No further contact was made so one can assume that normal healing took place.

Case Study 3 Human

Patient F. Age 60+. Occupation: Farming and Horse Breeder.

Symptoms: non-union (multiple compounded # to proximal end of right tibia).

Time post injury until Pmft: approx. two years.

Other complications: see below:

Treatment up to Pmft application: plated, pinned and wired across #. Ilizarov cage fitted during treatment.

Prognosis: very poor. Surgeon's report of potential for amputation of lower limb.

Referred for treatment using Pmft. suggested regime was 50Hz/constant with 3 x 20 minute treatments across # daily.

Progress was recorded by radiographs from onset of treatment.

Progress: 8 weeks' evidence of bridging.

Patient hospitalised during first months of treatment and showed firm evidence of bridging across segments and tibial shaft.

Full union after 12 months. Patient returned to normal activities and horse riding.

Comment:

This case, although in the lower limb, had severe trauma just below the knee and reflects the neurological deficit similar to that in case 1. The time post fracture to treatment was about one year and the healing, once treatment had commenced, was rapid. It may be the case that the neurological damage had begun to heal, thus helping establish currents of injury over the site. Pulsed magnetic therapy may have both stimulated neurological healing as well as assisting to resolve the fracture.

Case Study 4 Human

Patient F. Age 60+. Occupation: University Professor.

Symptoms: non-union # 4th and 5th metatarsals.

Time post injury until Pmft: approx. 1 Year.

Other complications: none known

Treatment up to Pmft: back slab plaster and binding.

Prognosis: one stated.

Referred for treatment using Pmft. suggested regime was 50Hz/constant with 3 x 20 minute treatments across # daily.

Progress was verbally related to results from scheduled hospital visits.

Progress: At six weeks evidence of bridging and weight bearing possible. At 3 months, patient returned to normal duties and discharged from hospital care.

Comment:

This patient was a non-medical university academic who had heard of the success of a university colleague who had had Pmft treatment. Again a degree of scepticism was noted but medical approval was obtained and treatment commenced. A possible reason for such non-unions within the foot would again be neurological although peripheral neuropathy was not reported. The speed at which this person's injury progressed may have been assisted by loadbearing in addition to Pmft.

Case Study 5 (Human) Neurological

Patient F. Age 38. Occupation: Disabled

Symptoms: Parkinson's disease

Time up to treatment with Pmft: several years since initial diagnosis.

Other complications: depression.

Treatment carried out with approval of hospital specialist managing patient's care.

Treatment regime: 50 Hz base, 17.5 pulse for 10 minutes followed by 200Hz constant for a further 10 minutes. Also, 15 rotations of subcranial bilateral therapeutic massage of the upper spine.

Frequency of treatment: twice weekly for 6 weeks.

Progress reported by patient was a reduction in the required amount of medication (agreed with her GP), Entacapone and other precursor dopamine substitutes.

Progress reported by consultant: Patient depression markedly reduced making handling of her condition more manageable.

Patient is now undergoing further treatment with experimental drugs. Depression has gone. Pmft discontinued.

Comment:

This is a difficult case to analyse. I had had some research involvement into other forms of neurological problems during my visits to Australia. These were coupled with research being carried out through Monash University. They were mainly patients suffering from early onset of dementia. Parkinson's disease is caused by lack of dopamine being produced by the substantia nigra area of the brain. Since dopamine is a neurotransmitter utilised in the motor cortex to control proprioceptive feedback from muscles, it was reasoned that if the neurons responsible for producing dopamine were damaged then Pmft may help re-establish membrane potentials and therefore allow function of the neurotransmitter. The fact that the patient's medication was reduced may lend some credibility to this theory but the lifting of depression is another area in which anecdotal reports have suggested Pmft helps relieve.

In a recent encounter on the street with this patient she was symptom free due to more modern medication. Since it was quite some time since her treatment with Pmft it is speculative whether the treatment had some long lasting effect or due to her attitude to further treatment. This positive attitude may have been the result of Pmft treatment. Her own feelings were that it certainly played a part. She is likely to be on medication for the rest of her life.

A Guide to Pulsed Magnetic Therapy

Case Study 6 Amputation

Patient F. Age 30-40.

Occupation: Disabled / Horse Trainer

Symptom: amputation of right foot

Other complications: depression.

This case was reported by patient. She carried out the treatment with the equipment purchased for her horses without the knowledge or approval of the consultant involved with her case and it was only reported back to me by the patient after she concluded her self-treatment. Although it does not fall under the medically confirmed categories since approval of her carers was not sought or its outcome confirmed by them, it has to be considered as largely anecdotal. The initial problem arose because of a distal third # that became diseased resulting in amputation. The stump failed to heal with sepsis setting in. Antibiotics and steroids used for treatment but without effect.

Prognosis: due to above complications the surgeon recommended removal of the whole of the lower limb. Patient refused.

She treated herself around the stump area with blue light phototherapy (1400 Hz @ 469nm) and pulsed magnetic therapy on settings of base 50, Pulse 17.5. Treatment duration for both modalities 10 minutes 4 times daily both as an in-patient and treatment at home.

Medical inspections showed that the stump started to dry up within a few days of the onset of treatment. Prognosis improved. Surgeon could not explain improvement. Patient referred for fitting of prosthetic foot and eventually discharged from care. Patient now returned to normal life and is once again competition riding.

Comment:

This case was included for interest because the patient reported it verbally and the carers involved were totally unaware the she was treating herself. Although the outcome was excellent the author would never countenance keeping the medical professionals involved in the dark. Her equipment was brought into the ward and kept hidden for the duration of her stay. The recommendations that I gave her were for the problems encountered of sepsis and soft tissue healing for her own animals with the assurance of her veterinary surgeon's involvement.

Case Study 7 Multiple Sclerosis

Patient F. Age 30-40.

Occupation: unknown

Symptoms: loss of right lower limb sensation, some incontinence.

Other complications: none known.

This patient was under the care of a specialist using experimental drugs that after several years had had no effect on symptoms. She indicated to him that she would like to try Pmft. He refused to agree so she changed specialist to one who took the attitude that he did not think it would be of any value, but to go ahead anyway.

Pmft was applied over her spine at 50Hz base and 17.5Hz pulse, after a simple neurological check of pin prick sensations down the front of her legs and plantar reflex under her foot. No sensations were recorded.

After approximately 2 months patient was again seen and reported that she was less incontinent and managed to gain more mobility now using walking aids. Previously wheelchair bound. Neurological tests repeated as before. Sensation was reported along the legs and there was a plantar reflex reaction.

The suggestion that pulsed magnetic therapy was in some way totally responsible for the reported improvements should be viewed, in this case, as just one of the factors that were involved.

1. It could be that the drugs had had some long lasting effect that kicked in after a time lapse from last medication.

2. Natural remissions do occur intermittently with MS sufferers.

3. Positive attitude of the patient.

Comment:

The theory of possible interactions Pmft may have had is in helping the myelin in the spine to tighten up its many dendrites like branches around up to 16 nerve fibres. If the body's auto immune system had broken down and attacked the oligodendrocyte cells, then perhaps some of those cells as yet not severely damaged may have had help in re-establishing their membrane potentials allowing nutrients to be again accepted and restoring their function.

This case, like the last one, is included for interest but shows that much more research is needed.

Case Study 8 Fracture

Patient F. Age 30-40.

Occupation: Dressage Coach

Symptoms: fracture to right tibia

Other complications: patient is paraplegic

This is a recently reported case where the patient used pulsed magnetic therapy on herself following a fracture caused by a fall out of her wheelchair. Medical referral suggested that there may be problems with this fracture healing due to hypotrophy of muscle and poor blood supply due to her disabled condition. Reduction and bracing of the limb took place and the patient was sent home. A friend, who had pulsed magnetic therapy equipment, loaned it to the patient who used it on herself. The medical authorities involved were unaware of this procedure.

Subsequent clinic visits and radiographs showed that the fracture had healed at the same rate and in the same way as would have been expected from an able-bodied patient. Surprise was expressed at this outcome.

Discussion

Again this case has been included for interest as it was self-motivated by the patient without normal medical approval. It has to be classed as anecdotal and the details are provided through a second party so cannot be formally verified. However, the facts suggest that the theories discussed in this book confirm that where normal bone pressures are absent and also natural piezo charges these can be substituted for by pulsed electromagnetic induction. Another aspect of this case is the poor blood supply that the consultant suggested would impair any healing. When used in veterinary cases, I always suggest a regime for orthopaedics problems of a base 50 pulsed at 17.5 for 10 minutes prior to a 20 minutes' treatment at 50Hz on constant. The combination of the two treatments suggests that the first of the treatments may open up the capillaries allowing better blood flow followed by treatment of the fracture site. It is believed that this patient followed this procedure, repeating the process several times per day.

Case Study #9 Equine Tendon Severance

Race Horse Injury

The sample of case histories listed have to this point been all human since as stated verification in most cases of the treatments and outcomes has been confirmed by medical opinion. This case was reported from a racing stables where veterinary opinion and subsequent investigation provided a confirmation of healing achieved.

The race horse had been recently purchased for £120,000 and been transported to its first outing at Edinburgh. The horse was kicked by another horse and suffered a severance of the superficial digital flexor tendon. The course duty vet suggested that the animal should be euthanized immediately. The owners refused and with the backing of their own vet transported the horse back to the training yard and straight away put it on box rest and under the supervision of both the veterinary surgeon and a therapist. The leg was bound and pulsed magnetic therapy applied almost from day one and several times per day thereafter along with other manual therapies. The pulsed magnetic therapy settings were a mixture of 50 Hz base pulsed at 17.5 Hz for 10 minutes and 50Hz on constant for longer periods. The 50/17.5 Hz was to aid soft tissue repairs and to help increase blood supply to the region. The 50/C was to aid the tendon to heal.

After several months the horse was then gradually returned to exercise and appeared to be normal in its gait. A year after injury the horse was declared fit to race again and completed its first run without incident. On its second outing, after its return to racing, it suffered a heart attack and died. A post mortem was carried out and at the request of the owners the previously severed tendon was analysed and appeared in every respect to be normal.

Discussion

The limited details above have been passed to me directly by the owner of both the horse and the training stable which is internationally well known and based in Scotland. Pulsed magnetic therapy has been one of the main modalities used at the stables for many years and is often the first to be used in any number of rehabilitation cases with varying amounts of success. The veterinary surgeon at the stables is a supporter of pulsed magnetic therapy and it was under his direction that the treatment of the case above was carried out. The sad outcome for the horse did provide a useful opportunity for the surgeon to take a look at the damaged tendon.

Appendix 2

EXPERIMENT ONE

Demonstration 1

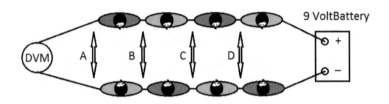

Requirements:

1. Digital voltmeter (DVM)
2. 6 to 9 volt battery
3. Sufficient 15 cm strips of bare wire

Stage One

Line up two rows of students and get them to hold on to a piece of wire to connect with their neighbour. The two students at point 'A' connect to the leads of a digital voltmeter set to 20 Volts. The two students nearest the battery connect to a terminal each. Note the reading on the digital voltmeter.

Stage Two

The two end students at point 'A' then remove the voltmeter and connect directly across the row completing a circuit.

Take the voltmeter and measure across the rows at positions 'B', 'C' and 'D'. Note the readings at each position.

Results:

Stage One results should indicate a voltage pretty much the same as the battery voltage. A small loss may occur but most of the voltage should still be indicated.

This means that the row connected to the negative terminal will become 'charged' negatively compared to the row connected to the positive terminal.

Stage two results shows that voltages can be measured across the rows and across each individual student. The voltage across each individual should equal the battery voltage divided by the number of students completing the circuit.

Discussion

This simple inexpensive experiment is very safe provided that the wires directly connected to the battery do not make contact. Care must be taken to avoid this happening as a high current will flow especially if a lead acid cell is used. Burning or melting of the wire is possible. The experiment shows that free electrons are available in tissue to form charges and to flow through the body without causing harm or sensation.

Appendix 2

EXPERIMENT 2

Simple electronic circuit used with students

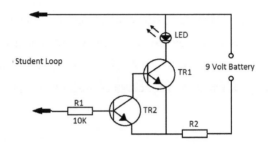

The above circuit is a called a 'Darlington Pair'. It is a high gain circuit that can amplify a very small current. The two transistors are of the general purpose NPN types. Its construction should be well within the capabilities of a competent technician. It provides a visual indication of a complete circuit formed by a ring of students simply touching the two leads when the circuit is energised by connecting to a battery.

We have used this circuit regularly at Nottingham School of Veterinary Medicine and Science with students attending the CEPT's veterinary physiotherapy course run using the school's facilities. The circuit works by TR1 being switched on by the very small positive charge felt via the 10K resistor from the positive line connected to the battery via a loop of subjects. This, in turn, turns on TR2 allowing the LEDs to illuminate.

This small turn on charge will be passed through any number of students forming the circuit. It, like experiment 1, serves to demonstrate the electrical nature of tissue and supports the theories discussed throughout this book. Thus it can be seen that electrons are freely available to form charges and that these charges can be induced to therapeutic effect by pulsed electromagnetism.

REFERENCES AND OTHER READING

- Barker AT & Freeston I (2007) Transcranial magnetic stimulation. Scholarpedia 2(10) 293
- Basset et al. (1974) Augmentation of bone repair by inductively coupled electromagnetic fields. Science May 3 1974: 184(136) 575-7
- Becker RO (1998) The Body Electric
- Bromiley M Equine Injury, Therapy and Rehabilitation. Blackwell 1993
- Coulter Exposure to PMF in treatment of plantar ulcers in leprosy patients. Tropical Disease Bulletin 1997
- De-Kun Li, MD, PhD; Hong Chen, MPH; Roxana Odouli, 2011 MSPH Maternal Exposure to Magnetic Fields During Pregnancy in Relation to the Risk of Asthma in Offspring
- Liu et al. PEMF influence both proteoglycan turnover and collagen synthesis by embryonic chick sternal cartilage explanted to culture. Ref in Proceedings of 1st World Congress in Magnetotherapy. 1996
- Demetski A & Kartashov N Clinical use of magnetic fields. Izhevsk 1977 81-2
- Detlavs et al. Mechanisms of biol. ffects of electromagnetic radiation Puschino 1987: 175--6
- Dipoldova G, Balneol J & Balneol L, 16(3) 1988 p71-75 Medical Practice Leningrad 1989
- Ezhova L et al. Vopr Kurortol, Fizioter. Lech.Fiz.Kult (1) 1985: 58-59
- Fukada, E and Yasuda, I , J. Phys. Soc. Japan, **12**, 1159 (1957).
- Fukada, E and Yasuda, I Jap. J. App. Physics, **3**, 117 (1964)

A Guide to Pulsed Magnetic Therapy

- Haas W et al. Karl Franz University, Graz, Austria 1993
- Inove N et al. (2002) Effect of PEMF on late phase osteotomy gap healing in a canine tibial model. J Orthop Res. Sept 2002:1106-14
- Jerabek J Proceedings of First World Congress in Magnetotherapy. London 1996
- Laycock (Somerville) DC Pulsed magnetic field therapy and the physiotherapist. 'In Touch' Journal of Organisation of Chartered Physios. In Private Practice No 81 Autumn 96: 8-9
- Lightwood. Dept of Surgery, Clinical Research Unit, Queen Elizabeth Hospital, Birmingham. Journal of Biomedical Engineering: Vol. 11, Sept 1989
- Liu et al. PEMF influence both proteoglycan turnover and collagen synthesis by embryonic chick sternal cartilage explanted to culture. Ref in Proceedings of 1st World Congress in Magnetotherapy. 1996
- Li-Yi Sun et al. (2009) Pulsed electromagnetic fields accelerate proliferation and osteogenic gene expression in human bone marrow mesenchymal stem cells during osteogenic differentiation. Bioelectromagnetics. October 2009
- Massari L et al (2009) Pulsed electromagnetic fields and low intensity pulsed ultrasound in bone tissues. Clin. Cases Mineral Bone Metab. May – Aug 2009 6(2) 149-154
- Ming-Tzu Tsai et al. (2009) Modulation of osteogenesis in human mesenchymal stem cells by specific pulsed electromagnetic field stimulation. J. Orthop Res. Sep 2009 27(9): 1169-74.
- Madronero Influence of MF on calcium salts crystal formation. BES Journal 1990
- Nagarajan et al. (2007) Effects of BMP-2 and pulsed electromagnetic field (PEMF) on rat primary osteoblastic cell proliferation and gene expression. J.Orthop. Research Vol. 25 Issue 9

- Nikolski Clinical use of mag. Fields. Izheusk 1977 p61- 63
- Pabst H and Kleine M Use of magnetic foil in treatment of sports injuries. 1983
- Pafkova H First World Congress for Electricity and Magnetism in Biology and Medicine p104
- Sansaverino E Riva (1990) 2nd International Congress on Magneto Medicine Nov 1990
- Sahinogu et al. PEMF's induce osteogenesis and up-regulate bone morphogenetic proteins 2 and 4mRNA in rat osteoblasts in vitro. Bone & Joint Research Unit, London. Ref in Proceedings of 1st World Congress in Magnetotherpy. 1996
- Sandyk R Resolution of longstanding symptoms of MS by application of picotesla range of magnetic fields. International Journal of Neuroscience 1993 70
- Sisken B, Knabe et al. Emerging Electromagnetic Medicine. 1990
- Sharrard WJ (1990) Double blind trial on fractures of tibial shaft 1981-87. Journal Bone & Joint Surgery May 1990: 72-B: 347-355
- Tetrakova L. Vopr. Kurortol. Fiziotr. Lech. Fiz. Kult(6) p63 1985
- Trock et al. (1994) Pulsed Magnetic Fields in the treatment of osteoarthritis of knee and cervical spine. J. of Rheumatology 1994, 21: 19
- Valentova D, Benda J. Balneol L 13(8) p153 -160
- Valentova and Dipldova Baleneol L 16(3) p75
- Warnke U. (1983) Possible role of PMF in reduction of pain. Elsevier Biomedical Press
- Yang Zhang et al. (2006) A study of the effects of flux density and frequency of electromagnetic field on neurite outgrowth in PC12 cells. J Biological Physics Feb 2006
- Zakharyuta F. Mechanism of Biol. Effects of EM Radiation. Puschino 1987 p173-74 Unknown Positive Health Dec/Jan 1997

ABOUT THE AUTHOR: DAVID C SOMERVILLE.

David has had a varied life and career. Born in Sheffield he attended a secondary modern school having missed a large part of the year of the 11 plus exam due to polio and an accident. At this time David had a name change to Laycock by adoption of his step-father. In later life he reverted back to Somerville. In the secondary school he showed a good aptitude for science but left without qualifications. He worked as a van boy and then a shoe salesman until winning a place at a Royal Air Force Boy Entrants School to study sciences, maths and air radio engineering. He served in the regular Royal Air Force until the age of 27, seeing active service in Borneo flying as a helicopter crewman and test pilot's assistant on small jet aircraft. He was then commissioned into the RAF Reserves and served for a further 16 years, retiring as a Squadron Leader.

On leaving the regular service he worked as a research technician at Sheffield University then a computer technician with ICL. After 6 years he left ICL as a senior engineering analyst and after a short time in management with Marconi Space and Defence became a full time student studying physics, chemistry and education at what was to become Manchester Metropolitan University. Qualifying as a science teacher he decided to study orthopaedics at Salford University, Department of Orthopaedic Mechanics having studied the effects on bones caused by pollution and fluoride poisoning as a final year undergraduate research project. He also lectured in electronic engineering at Newcastle College, Staffs in order to supplement and help finance whilst a post graduate student. He studied for nearly 6 years at Salford, initially for an MSc then a PhD researching human long bone fractures and analysis. On leaving Salford he was appointed as senior lecturer and research advisor at both Manchester Metropolitan and Salford Universities to PhD and MSc students studying aspects of orthopaedics and orthotics. During this time, he became fascinated in the use of pulsed magnetism and its ability to stimulate non-union fractures and its beneficial effects on injured soft tissue.

Since leaving university he has lectured worldwide on the subject and written published articles on the therapeutic aspects of pulsed magnetism as a medical tool. He has been supported throughout his professional life by his wife, Marjorie who herself is an accomplished scientist and educationalist. David is also a qualified pilot. He was a founding member of the Institute of Registered Veterinary and Animal Physiotherapists (IRVAP).